11+ Verbal Reasoning

When it comes to 11+ preparation, nothing beats practice — and this CGP book is packed with the best practice you'll find, all at the perfect level for ages 10-11.

It starts with questions that focus on one topic at a time, so children can really get to grips with each key skill. Once they're confident, there's a selection of mixed-topic Assessment Tests to help them get used to the style of the real 11+ papers.

We've also included detailed, step-by-step answers. Everything you need!

Practice Book – Ages 10-11
with Assessment Tests

How to use this Practice Book

This book is divided into two parts — themed question practice and full-length assessment tests. There are answers and detailed explanations at the back of the book.

Themed question practice

- Each page contains practice questions divided by topic. Use these pages to work out your child's strengths and the areas they find tricky. The questions get harder down each page.

- Your child can use the smiley face tick boxes to evaluate how confident they feel with each topic.

Assessment tests

- The second part of the book contains eight assessment tests, each with a mix of question types from the first half of the book.

- You can print multiple-choice answer sheets so your child can practise the tests as if they're sitting the real thing — visit cgpbooks.co.uk/11plus/answer-sheets or scan the QR code.

- Use the printable answer sheets if you want your child to do each test more than once.

- If you want to give your child timed practice, give them a time limit of 40 minutes for each test, and ask them to work as quickly and carefully as they can.

- The tests get harder from 1-8, so don't be surprised if your child finds the later ones more tricky.

- Your child should aim for a mark of around 85% (63 questions correct) in each test. If they score less than this, use their results to work out the areas they need more practice on.

- If they haven't managed to finish the test in time, they need to work on increasing their speed, whereas if they have made a lot of mistakes, they need to work more carefully.

- Keep track of your child's scores using the progress chart at the back of the book.

Published by CGP

Editors:
Claire Boulter, Siân Butler, Heather Cowley, Robbie Driscoll, Rebecca Greaves, Georgina Paxman

With thanks to Andy Cashmore for the proofreading.
With thanks to Jan Greenway for the copyright research.

p.67: Extract from *Nightfall in New York*. Reprinted by permission of HarperCollins Publishers Ltd © 2021 Katherine Woodfine

p.85: Extract from *Lost on Mars*. © Paul Magrs 2015

p.97: Poem "Vacation" from PLAYLIST FOR THE APOCALYPSE: POEMS by Rita Dove. Copyright © 2021 by Rita Dove. Used by permission of W. W. Norton & Company, Inc.

A note for teachers, parents and caregivers
Just something to bear in mind if you're choosing further reading for 10-11 year olds — all the extracts in this book are suitable for children of this age, but we can't vouch for the full texts they're take from, or other works by the same authors.

ISBN: 978 1 78908 805 2

Printed by Elanders Ltd, Newcastle upon Tyne.
Clipart from Corel®

Based on the classic CGP style created by Richard Parsons.

Contents

Tick off the check box for each topic as you go along.

Alphabet Positions

Answer the questions below. Use the alphabet to help you.

A B C D E F G H I J K L M N O P Q R S T U V W X Y Z

Look at this example:

Which letter is at position **8** in the alphabet?   __H__

1. Which letter is at position **10** in the alphabet?   _____

2. Which letter is at position **16** in the alphabet?   _____

3. If the alphabet was written backwards,
    which letter would be at position **5**?   _____

4. If the alphabet was written backwards,
    which letter would be at position **20**?   _____

/ 4

What is the alphabet position of the last letter of the word:

5. **DANGEROUS**?   _____

6. **CHAMELEON**?   _____

What is the alphabet position of the middle letter of the word:

7. **ANNIVERSARY**?   _____

8. **CHALLENGE**?   _____

/ 4

9. If all the letters in the word **MAGAZINE** were removed from the
    alphabet, which letter would be at position 7 in the new alphabet?   _____

10. If all the letters in the word **WHIMSICAL** were removed from
    the alphabet, what alphabet position would the letter Q occupy?   _____

11. If all the letters in the word **MALARKEY** were removed from
    the alphabet, what alphabet position would the letter F occupy?   _____

12. If all the letters in the word **KINGDOM** were removed from
    the alphabet, what alphabet position would the letter V occupy?   _____

/ 4

Hint: Although you'll normally be given the alphabet for questions like
these, if you do need to write it out, check that you've done it correctly.

Identify a Letter from a Clue

Find the letter that the clue refers to.
Make sure your answer is correct for all parts of the clue.

Look at this example:

Find the letter that occurs most often in **ACCELERATE**. ___E__

Find the letter that occurs:

1. once in **TREEHOUSE** and twice in **TOMORROW**. _____

2. three times in **ECCENTRICITY**. _____

3. most often in **COLLECTIBLE**. _____

4. most often in **ENVIRONMENTS**. _____

5. most often in **PARAPHRASES**. _____

Hint: Circle the letters in each word that fit the clue so you can easily see what the answer could be.

/ 5

6. once in **ELIGIBLE** and twice in **BEGRUDGE**. _____

7. once in **LIMPETS**, twice in **FINISHES**
   and three times in **ACTIVITIES**. _____

8. most often in **FESTIVALS**, **SAUSAGES** and **DISCUSSED**. _____

9. twice in **PRESENTATION** and twice in **CRITTERS**. _____

10. once in **DELIRIUM**, once in **DISMANTLE**,
    but not in **DIAMETER**. _____

/ 5

11. twice in **SEMICIRCLE**, twice in **SEMIPRECIOUS**
    and three times in **SEMIRETIRED**. _____

12. twice in **CATERPILLAR**, twice in **RECTANGULAR**
    and once in **TEACUPS**. _____

13. once in **ENTHUSIASTIC**, once in **SUNDRENCHED**
    and twice in **HONEYBUNCH**. _____

14. twice in **MANAGEMENT**, twice in **UNEMPLOYMENT**
    and once in **MALICIOUS**. _____

/ 4

Alphabetical Order

Answer the questions below. Use the alphabet to help you.

A B C D E F G H I J K L M N O P Q R S T U V W X Y Z

Look at this example:

> Which letter in the word **ORANGE** comes
> nearest the end of the alphabet?   _R_

If you arrange the following words in alphabetical order, which comes third?

1. Pineapple, Pianist, Pistachio, Piggybacked, Pitchfork   _____

2. Mistake, Mischief, Missiles, Mishandled, Miscellaneous   _____

If you arrange the following words in alphabetical order, which comes last?

3. Anthropology, Antonym, Antiquated, Antelopes   _____

4. Descent, Dessert, Deserted, Destination, Despondent   _____

/ 4

---

5. Which letter in the word **SCORPION** comes nearest the end of the alphabet?   _____

6. Which letter in the word **WRINGING** comes nearest the start of the alphabet?   _____

7. Which letter in the word **PROFOUND** comes nearest the start of the alphabet?   _____

8. Which letter in the word **NAUSEA** comes nearest the end of the alphabet?   _____

/ 4

If you spell the following words backwards, then put them in alphabetical order, which word comes second?

9. Comprehension, Percussion, Aspersion, Expulsion   _____

10. Bravery, Granary, Trickery, Robbery, Enquiry   _____

Hint: Focus on the letters rather than the meaning of the words.

If you spell the following words backwards, then put them in alphabetical order, which word comes fourth?

11. Convertible, Crumble, Shamble, Resemble, Stable   _____

12. Specify, Disqualify, Mystify, Humidify, Satisfy   _____

/ 4

Plurals

Plurals

Write the correct plural of the word in brackets. Look at this example:

Sarah admired the _poppies_ (**poppy**) in the field.

1. The _____ (**spy**) were creeping quietly after the criminal.

2. Mia heard the horses' _____ (**hoof**) thundering past her.

3. The charity raised money to protect the coral _____ (**reef**).

4. Aaron made a delicious pie using the leftover _____ (**peach**).

5. The weather forecast warned that there would be several _____ (**tornado**).

6. The painter had two different _____ (**studio**) in which to work.

7. As autumn turned to winter, the _____ (**leaf**) fell from the trees.

8. Harry could hear the faint _____ (**echo**) of voices in the empty hall.

9. Mo's mum was angry when she saw the _____ (**scuff**) on his shoes.

/ 9

Plurals

Write the correct plural of the word in brackets. Look at this example:

Khalid needed to get his ___feet___ (**foot**) measured.

10. Andy chased the _____ (**goose**) out of the garden by waving his arms.

11. Samia watched the _____ (**fisherman**) as they sailed away.

12. Karley brushed her _____ (**tooth**) before leaving the house.

13. There was an outbreak of head _____ (**louse**) at school.

14. The farmer's cows watched their _____ (**offspring**) playing together.

15. We saw three _____ (**species**) of bird on our nature hike this morning.

16. A number of people offered incorrect _____ (**diagnosis**) of the problem.

17. There are different types of _____ (**fungus**) growing in the wood.

18. The writer frequently used _____ (**ellipsis**) to create tension in his work.

Hint: Some exception words are the same in the singular and plural.

/ 9

Homophones

Homophones

Choose the correct homophone from the brackets.
Look at this example:

Kirsty _knew_ (**knew** **new**) the answer.

1. Our neighbour saw a _____ (**links** **lynx**) when she visited Canada.

2. As Huan opened the _____ (**gate** **gait**), it creaked sinisterly.

3. The words in _____ (**bold** **bowled**) stand out from the rest of the text.

4. Ed was angry when Stephen broke the window _____ (**pain** **pane**).

5. Betty and Paul took a _____ (**crews** **cruise**) around the Norwegian fjords.

6. The rainbow was a colourful _____ (**ark** **arc**) across the sky.

7. Juana _____ (**wrung** **rung**) out her swimming costume and left it to dry.

8. The bridge was an impressive _____ (**feat** **feet**) of engineering.

9. Richard suffered a serious _____ (**laps** **lapse**) in judgement.

/ 9

Homophones

Underline the correct homophone to complete the sentence.
Look at this example:

I'd like (**to** **two** **too**) leave the house.

10. Maddy watched Daniel (**poor** **pore** **pour**) the water into the cup.

11. Tom tried to (**seas** **seize** **sees**) the trophy from Cho's hand.

12. "(**You're** **Your** **Yore**) going to be late for school!" shouted Jenny.

13. The breakdown truck (**toad** **toed** **towed**) our car to the garage.

14. The bride walked down the (**isle** **aisle** **I'll**) towards the front of the church.

15. Poppy began to (**wale** **whale** **wail**) when she stubbed her big toe.

16. It didn't take long for Nathan to walk home because he lived close (**by** **bye** **buy**).

17. (**There** **They're** **Their**) garden had become overgrown during the winter.

18. The archaeological (**site** **cite** **sight**) was located at the edge of the cliff.

Hint: If you're not sure what a word means, focus on the words you do know to see if one of these fits the sentence.

/ 9

Prefixes and Suffixes

Choose the correct prefix from the list to complete the word in each sentence: **un**, **im**, **pre**, **sub**, **re** or **de**. Look at this example:

Hannah waited _im_ patiently for the parcel to arrive.

1. Yanlin was asked to _____order his food before going to the restaurant.

2. The _____titles on the film were so small that Kate couldn't read them.

3. Charlotte had to _____paint the kitchen after Joey drew on the walls.

4. After the argument, Ben thought it was _____likely they would visit again.

5. Archie added up the cost of each item to check the _____total before tax.

6. Although Charlie's explanation was _____probable, I believed him.

7. It is _____professional to arrive late for work on a regular basis.

8. Josef _____played the embarrassing moment over and over in his head.

9. Padma felt _____hydrated because she hadn't drunk enough water.

Hint: Read the whole sentence to make sure your prefix makes sense.

/ 9

Complete these sentences by adding a suffix to the word in brackets. Look at this example:

The pupils could play several _musical_ (**music**) instruments.

10. Scott paid for his gym _____ (**member**) on an annual basis.

11. The weather for the hike was _____ (**glory**) and sunny.

12. Walid had an _____ (**impress**) number of running medals.

13. The football team's _____ (**weak**) was their defence.

14. The chef's new dish was _____ (**taste**), so he added more salt.

15. The girls had a _____ (**success**) day at the fair and won many prizes.

16. Oliver was pleased with the _____ (**animate**) he created on his computer.

17. The school is looking for someone _____ (**rely**) to work in the office.

18. Winning first prize in the competition was a great _____ (**achieve**).

/ 9

Section Two — Spelling and Grammar

Awkward Spellings

Complete these words by adding the correct vowel.
Look at this example:

Pam attended a conf_e_rence run by her comp_a_ny.

1. Hayley was eas__ly the strongest swimmer in her age categ__ry.

2. The bus__ness was charged a high rate of int__rest by the bank.

3. Carl was miser__ble at the thought of eating all his veg__tables.

4. Ashni was confident that she had good gen__ral knowl__dge.

5. The builders argued over the bound__ry of the priv__te driveway.

6. Mrs Dornan gave her secret__ry a good ref__rence when she got a new job.

7. Punam was respons__ble for volunt__ry work at her local animal shelter.

8. The origin__l plans for the new shopping centre had to be aband__ned.

9. There are many ben__fits to walking compared to being sedent__ry.

> Hint: The gaps are all unstressed vowels — the vowel sound may not be clear or be spelt as you'd expect.

/ 9

Complete these words with the correct pair of consonants so that the sentence makes sense. Look at this example:

The plu_mb_er's van was parked o_pp_osite our house.

10. Niamh had ____itten her sister's new a____ress on the envelope.

11. The garden ____ome had to____led over in the bad weather.

12. Suyin ha____ily played several ____ords on the piano.

13. Otis was late to the party because of the te____ible tra____ic.

14. Mrs Brown shu____ered when she saw all the sweet wra____ers in the bin.

15. The runner was i____itated that he had pulled a mu____le in his leg.

16. John dou____ed that he would finish his e____ay by the deadline.

17. The de____ert was made from a mixture of sugar, flour, butter and egg yo____s.

18. Simon usually likes eating sa____on, but today he's lost his a____etite.

> Hint: Each letter pair is either a pair of double letters or has one silent letter.

/ 9

Mixed Spelling Questions

Each sentence contains a spelling mistake. Underline the word with the error and write the correct spelling on the line. Look at this example:

The haunted house was a <u>frightning</u> experience. _frightening_

1. Rose was intimidated by the giraffs when she reached their enclosure. _____

2. The pig devoured the apple, including the pips and stork, with a grunt. _____

3. Dave felt under presure to perform well in the competition. _____

4. Kai concealed his irational fear of donkeys; he was very embarrassed. _____

5. After reading the invitation, Lizzie chose a more informul outfit. _____

6. While the weather was settled, Grant quickly mode the lawn. _____

/ 6

7. Our nieghbours invited us to celebrate their silver wedding anniversary. _____

8. The doctor is an expert in diagnosing rare infectous diseases. _____

9. Yesterday afternoon was incredibly memerable for several reasons. _____

10. Be aware that certain types of mushroom can be poisunous if eaten. _____

11. The school has various policys to help improve students' attendance. _____

12. The divers discovered treasure in the reckage of the sunken ship. _____

/ 6

13. It was easy to decieve the detective because he was distracted. _____

14. Lindsey was fasinated by the city centre's colourful illuminations. _____

15. Acording to the legend, fairies and elves live under this bridge. _____

16. Unfortunately, the leisure centre extension is currently imcomplete. _____

17. The recent editian of the local newspaper was very well-received. _____

18. The visitor was an unwelcome interuption to Jo's daily routine. _____

/ 6

Mixed Spelling Questions

Underline the correct word to complete each sentence.
Look at this example:

> I didn't recognise Jules when I (**passed** past) him in the street.

1. Swimming is not allowed in this area due to strong (**currents** **currants**).

2. The pudding contained (**currents** **currants**), raisins and sultanas.

3. The managers (**accept** **except**) that the complaint could have been handled better.

4. Everything has been tidied away (**accept** **except**) the shoes and coats.

5. The calculator is missing from the (**stationary** **stationery**) cupboard.

6. Carol was stuck in (**stationary** **stationery**) traffic and hadn't moved for hours.

/ 6

7. You need to (**practice** **practise**) your handwriting to make it neater.

8. It takes years of (**practice** **practise**) to ride horses confidently.

9. I frequently (**lose** **loose**) my keys because I am very forgetful.

10. There was a (**lose** **loose**) screw in the table which caused it to break.

11. Camille asked if she could (**borrow** **lend**) my new cardigan for her party.

12. I will (**borrow** **lend**) you some money, but you must pay me back tomorrow.

/ 6

13. Tariq read the mysterious note (**aloud** **allowed**) so his family could hear.

14. On Saturdays, we are (**aloud** **allowed**) to stay up late and watch a film.

15. Please (**ensure** **insure**) that you have fastened your seat belt before take-off.

16. It is important to (**ensure** **insure**) your possessions against fire and theft.

17. The nature reserve had a positive (**effect** **affect**) on local wildlife.

18. When the motorway is closed, it will (**effect** **affect**) our journey home.

/ 6

Section Two — Spelling and Grammar

Verbs

Verbs & Subjects

Underline the word or words in each sentence which match the part of speech in brackets. Look at this example:

Elliot caught the last train home. **(subject)**

1. The sheep leapt over the broken fence and ran across the field. **(subject)**

2. The mountain guide showed us many interesting flowers. **(verb)**

3. In the kitchen, Reuben was singing quietly to himself . **(subject)**

4. Unlike yesterday, the warm sun shone brightly all day. **(verb)**

> Hint: These are all active sentences, so the verb usually follows the subject.

5. Mr Clarke passed Ellen a tin full of chocolate chip biscuits. **(subject)**

6. Parv and Jamie watched in horror at the cake falling from the plate. **(subject)**

7. The angry knock at the door echoes through the empty house. **(verb)**

8. At the sound of the car horn, Keith glanced in his mirror. **(verb)**

9. Swimming is excellent exercise for the whole body. **(subject)**

/ 9

Verbs

Underline the correct verb from the brackets to complete each sentence. Look at this example:

Felicity **(have has am)** forgotten her lunch.

10. Before the race started, the runner **(did do done)** some final stretches.

11. **(Gone Went Go)** through the gate, then turn right at the farm.

12. Emma **(drove driven drives)** slowly when she is nervous.

13. The sunflowers that Abigail planted **(is are be)** growing very tall.

14. It's crucial that we **(explains explain explaining)** these sales figures.

15. Mrs Gomez **(ate eats eaten)** her salad and took a sip of water.

16. If I **(were am was)** you, I would see a doctor soon.

17. Janek had **(ring rang rung)** the doorbell three times.

18. I will be **(give given gave)** my timetable on the first day of school.

/ 9

Verbs and Conjunctions

Verbs

Complete each sentence using the correct form of the verb in brackets. Write your answer on the line. Look at this example:

The caretaker has ___locked___ (**to lock**) the gates.

1. Aleksy _____ (**to forgive**) his sister when she broke his toy.

2. The cat has _____ (**to hide**) my scarf and I can't find it.

3. Last year, Ewan _____ (**to be**) a regular member of chess club.

4. If you _____ (**to know**) the answer, why didn't you say so?

5. When the bell rings, _____ (**to go**) inside and be quiet!

6. I will _____ (**to get**) you a jumper if you feel cold.

7. Tamsin was walking through the park when she _____ (**to find**) the money.

8. The teacher is _____ (**to write**) on the board while the pupils read.

9. Jim always _____ (**to fly**) first class when he travels for work.

> Hint: Make sure your answer agrees with the tense of the rest of the sentence.

/ 9

Conjunctions

Underline the most appropriate conjunction from the brackets to complete each sentence. Look at this example:

Alex borrowed the book (**after** <u>**while**</u> **if**) Greg was out.

10. Ifeoma was disappointed (**until while when**) the concert was cancelled.

11. I drink camomile tea (**because whether before**) it helps me sleep.

12. Shopping bores me, (**whereas or until**) playing netball is fantastic.

13. The tide was out, (**if so because**) we decided to walk along the beach.

14. You can choose three different sandwiches (**than until if**) you are hungry.

15. I will join your book group (**because while unless**) there isn't enough space.

16. Julia explored the castle (**and while unless**) she found it fascinating.

17. The package arrived (**but before if**) we left the house this morning.

18. Dogs make great pets, (**whereas or although**) they need lots of exercise.

/ 9

Section Two — Spelling and Grammar

Mixed Grammar Questions

Underline the word in each sentence which matches the part of speech in brackets. Look at this example:

Sophie <u>closed</u> the book with a sigh. **(verb)**

1. The elderly gentleman walked cautiously down the road. **(adjective)**

2. The cows glanced at Stephanie as she passed by. **(common noun)**

3. In the middle of the night, an owl drifted silently past the church. **(verb)**

4. Haruki wondered about the possibility of an early lunch. **(verb)**

5. I was surprised when the horror film ended badly. **(adverb)**

6. The bear waited for a while before leaving its den. **(conjunction)**

Hint: Look at the glossary on p.109 if you need a reminder about any of these parts of speech.

7. Cities had always intimidated Anna: they were so busy. **(proper noun)**

8. Jenna could almost smell the excitement in the air. **(adverb)**

9. Nobody could understand why the questions were so challenging. **(adjective)**

/ 9

Each sentence has one grammatical error. Underline the word which is wrong and write the correct word on the line. Look at this example:

Chloe has <u>ate</u> her vegetables.   *eaten*

10. Mark and Dina couldn't remember which car was their.   _____

11. Please don't bring no sharp or flammable items on the bus.   _____

12. Two students was performing in the game's halftime show.   _____

13. Write your name at the top, then turns the page.   _____

14. Karrie must attends the appointment, or it will be cancelled.   _____

15. I did good in my test, even though I was nervous.   _____

16. My cousin and me are travelling to Boston for a holiday.   _____

17. The window pane was broke by the naughty children.   _____

18. The dress what she wore featured a distinctive pattern.   _____

/ 9

Mixed Grammar Questions

Underline the most appropriate word from the brackets to complete each sentence. Look at this example:

Greta (do does **did** done) all her homework last night.

1. I told Max not to (crossed crossing crosses **cross**) the road without me.

2. Helen works (hardly **harder** hard hardest) than anyone else I know.

3. Don't (drank drunk **drink** drinks) my coffee before I get back!

4. I couldn't believe that the winning ticket was (**mine** I me my).

5. My favourite jumper has stretched (though **since** if why) you borrowed it.

6. If I ate healthier food, I would (**sleep** slept sleeping sleeps) better.

/ 6

7. My jacket was (tore **torn** tear tears) by the barbed wire fence.

8. I repeated the number (why what **which** how) they had given me.

9. Can we find them (unless despite **before** until) it gets dark?

10. Theo (woke **wakes** wake awake) early and dresses quietly.

11. You can't (is been was **be**) serious about going out in that rain.

12. It is important that you (working works worked **work**) in the family shop.

/ 6

13. There are too (much fewer less **many**) plates on the table.

14. (Buys **Buy** Buying Bought) these boots — now half price!

15. The trophy is (our us **ours** we) because we won the tournament.

16. Ryan (chose **chooses** chooses chosen) apple pie every time we come here.

17. The water (quick **quickly** fast faster) reached our front door.

/ 6

18. We saw llamas on our walk, (because **but** so if) they were sleeping.

Missing Letters

Find the letter that will finish the first word and start the second word of each pair. The same letter must be used for both pairs.

Look at this example:

hol (?) ry   lan (?) oom   __d__ (**hold**, **dry**, **land** and **doom**.)

1. wis (?) at   pac (?) arn   _____
2. gal (?) way   dat (?) rid   _____
3. dre (?) and   sno (?) asp   _____
4. woo (?) end   ge (?) ive   _____
5. soa (?) ust   sti (?) are   _____
6. lin (?) id   wea (?) ept   _____
7. ski (?) one   bea (?) ewt   _____

/ 7

8. twi (?) lum   pi (?) ave   _____
9. ou (?) ide   ne (?) ie   _____
10. gol (?) ive   hal (?) it   _____
11. mos (?) ake   bu (?) lot   _____
12. fel (?) ook   ow (?) id   _____
13. ha (?) ice   ai (?) ist   _____
14. tra (?) ear   an (?) ard   _____

/ 7

15. bee (?) ade   el (?) ir   _____
16. hi (?) eek   ni (?) rey   _____
17. sa (?) ry   ste (?) arm   _____
18. cal (?) ace   fai (?) ow   _____
19. tu (?) id   com (?) olt   _____
20. mo (?) ail   cla (?) ait   _____

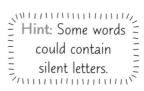

Hint: Some words could contain silent letters.

/ 6

Move a Letter

Remove one letter from the first word and add it to the second word to make two new words. Do not change the order of the other letters. Write the letter that moves on the line.

Look at this example:

event	hop	__e__	(The new words are **vent** and **hope**.)

1. plate   bee   _____

2. maker   ant   _____

3. ideal   bow   _____

4. whose   ash   _____

5. there   ten   _____

6. first   eve   _____

7. forth   ill   _____

> Hint: The letter that you move could fit anywhere in the second word.

/ 7

8. flash   let   _____

9. below   sit   _____

10. bound   fry   _____

11. going   man   _____

12. track   old   _____

13. swift   say   _____

14. carve   pot   _____

/ 7

15. fibre   red   _____

16. coast   sty   _____

17. crowd   lay   _____

18. range   wig   _____

19. solid   son   _____

20. avoid   led   _____

/ 6

Hidden Word

In each sentence below, a four-letter word is hidden at the end of one word and the start of the next. Underline the part of the sentence that contains the hidden word and write the hidden word on the line.

Look at this example:

The large glo<u>be st</u>opped spinning quickly.   ___best___

1. Harry's modern sofa irritates me.   _____

2. They stash old keepsakes away.   _____

3. That joke really backfired on you.   _____

4. Children tend to choose cake every time.   _____

5. I cannot explain how funny she was.   _____

6. We practise skiing on the slope nearby.   _____

7. I had to sweep almonds off the floor.   _____

/ 7

8. Our town council acknowledged the complaint.   _____

9. They strolled along the famous avenue.   _____

10. My kitten doesn't like the sound of snoring.   _____

11. That chef is known for cooking pasta skilfully.   _____

12. We decided to find the goat ourselves.   _____

13. The cobra blends into the undergrowth.   _____

14. It's great that twenty people have finished.   _____

/ 7

15. The famous group only performed three songs.   _____

16. My umbrella kept breaking when it rained.   _____

17. I help lottery winners invest in gold.   _____

18. Studying music opened many doors for him.   _____

19. I refuse to play water polo anymore.   _____

20. Ro will invite many people to the party.   _____

/ 6

Section Three — Making Words

Find the Missing Word

Find the three letter word that completes the word in capital letters, and so finishes the sentence in a sensible way.
Write your answer on the line.

Look at this example:

> My family are going on **HOAY** to France. _____LID_____

1. Arlo's **PNTS** bought him a bike for his birthday. _____

2. I was full of **REF** when I caught the train on time. _____

3. I'd like to work for a **COMY** that produces comedy films. _____

4. Natalie, a long-distance runner, is naturally **ATHIC**. _____

5. The magician made a rabbit **APR** out of thin air. _____

6. Lots of people used to work at the clothing **FORY**. _____

7. The map **INDIED** where the treasure was buried. _____

/ 7

8. **CLING** up my dog's muddy paw prints is not fun. _____

9. Dawn carefully turned the **PS** of her book. _____

10. Yusra is very **CRIVE** when it comes to drawing pictures. _____

11. I had a **TERLE** journey — I got lost at least six times. _____

12. We **ASED** that it wouldn't rain, but we were wrong. _____

13. To reach the other side of the river, we crossed a **BGE**. _____

14. The players needed a new **STRGY** to win the game. _____

/ 7

15. Sometimes, our teacher lets us choose our own **PNERS**. _____

16. Kaya wanted to buy some grapes, but **NOWE** was selling any. _____

17. My sister has a **TENCY** to giggle when the room goes quiet. _____

18. I had an ice cream with **CAEL** sauce on top. _____

19. It took a lot of **EFT** for Millie to carry her suitcase upstairs. _____

20. Although the house appeared **ORARY**, it held a unique secret. _____

/ 6

Section Three — Making Words

Use a Rule to Make a Word

The words in the second set follow the same pattern as the words in the first set. Find the missing word to complete the second set.

Look at this example:

dose (let) flat   area (_oat_) host

1. bath (hat) sway   mere (_____) plan

2. pain (can) rack   ship (_____) note

3. load (glad) goal   gold (_____) hive

4. peak (ape) harp   home (_____) twin

5. trip (rat) part   shut (_____) lane

6. name (men) team   move (_____) bang

7. lack (ask) sank   pace (_____) them

Hint: Keep your working-out neat to help you keep track of the letter combinations you've tried.

/ 7

8. wage (wig) wing   rush (_____) find

9. rate (tea) eats   held (_____) chip

10. lean (vein) evil   fled (_____) able

11. grid (drip) pair   sand (_____) time

12. ache (each) hear   need (_____) pier

13. slow (lose) sole   able (_____) rift

14. late (tale) seat   runs (_____) bear

/ 7

15. arms (ram) mare   knot (_____) door

16. earn (near) real   club (_____) doze

17. wake (hawk) wash   army (_____) smug

18. read (dear) dare   poor (_____) flew

19. rated (tear) terms   valid (_____) forum

20. fire (reef) fear   race (_____) fish

/ 6

Section Three — Making Words

Compound Words

Underline a word from the first set, followed by a word from the second set, that go together to form a new word.

Look at this example:

(care <u>any</u> fly)   (wash wear <u>thing</u>)   (The word is **anything**.)

1. (fast key pat)   (turn whole board)

2. (mare pony walk)   (tail step trust)

3. (lend real book)   (mark sell eyes)

4. (home draw fast)   (line made went)

5. (whole back wear)   (time pack ever)

6. (hand out no)   (site sent body)

7. (may deep week)   (see hum end)

/ 7

8. (prom count advert)   (ice down least)

9. (for top some)   (mule gift tune)

10. (past short note)   (rate table age)

11. (over miss home)   (chief come here)

12. (wild brake round)   (out life nest)

13. (near far is)   (shoe saw land)

14. (hold role hid)   (away den flat)

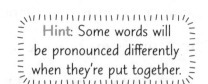

/ 7

15. (main not cap)   (tin soul ice)

16. (far leg come)   (end ward pair)

17. (clean sure like)   (wise nest line)

18. (for be both)   (her half seen)

19. (car peace plea)   (full sure sang)

20. (door do out)   (point sign main)

Hint: Some words will be pronounced differently when they're put together.

/ 6

Forming New Words

Find a word which, when put at the start or end of each set of three words, makes three new words. Write your answer on the line.

Look at this example:

| word | port | code | ____pass____ |

Find a word that can go **in front** of each of these words to form three new compound words.

1. time   dream   light   _____

2. moon   comb   bee   _____

3. hold   rest   path   _____

4. doors   fuse   come   _____

5. guard   boat   time   _____

6. cut   bread   list   _____

7. hole   kind   hunt   _____

8. day   mark   place   _____

/ 8

Find a word that can go **after** each of these words to form three new compound words.

9. down   snow   water   _____

10. second   back   before   _____

11. fair   camp   battle   _____

12. frame   patch   paper   _____

13. goal   inn   house   _____

14. brain   man   will   _____

15. air   water   skin   _____

16. run   melt   show   _____

/ 8

Section Three — Making Words

Complete a Word Pair

Find the word that completes the third pair of words so that it follows the same pattern as the first two pairs.

Look at this example:

earn ear   bank ban   seat _____sea_____

1. sand send   land lend   band   _____

2. after raft   logic clog   earth   _____

3. steady east   legacy gale   invest   _____

4. power row   eager rag   needs   _____

5. agenda and   moment men   answer   _____

6. knits stink   snips spins   spots   _____

7. ready year   north horn   print   _____

/ 7

8. itself felt   report tore   stream   _____

9. catch chat   solid idol   false   _____

10. bear beat   load loaf   mail   _____

11. sudden dens   mother term   entire   _____

12. speech seep   advise avid   income   _____

13. split pits   apple plea   sweet   _____

14. animal mail   planet neat   player   _____

/ 7

15. prevent veer   student duet   chapter   _____

16. rail nail   gold cold   week   _____

17. attract cat   elderly led   anybody   _____

18. tactical act   identify fin   software   _____

19. intended den   increase are   shortage   _____

20. message sea   enhance hen   expense   _____

/ 6

Section Three — Making Words

Anagram in a Sentence

Rearrange the letters in capitals to spell a word that completes the sentence in a sensible way. Write the new word on the line.

Look at this example:

I bought a **EZDON** eggs. _____DOZEN_____

1. We could hear a **RBID** chirping in the tree. _____

2. Nina gave a **CESPEH** in front of the whole school. _____

3. Josh's music teacher is an **PTEREX** at the guitar. _____

4. I found my dog snooping around in the **CKNEITH**. _____

5. Guards stopped the **ETSACL** from being invaded. _____

6. The **LAOPEARNE** soared through the clouds. _____

7. The hurricane caused a lot of **GEMADA**. _____

/ 7

8. The scientist discovered two new **CSPIESE** of butterfly. _____

9. I **MIEPORS** that I will tidy my bedroom later. _____

10. We phoned the restaurant to **VREESER** a table. _____

11. That **NCTEIAN** statue is over three thousand years old. _____

12. The team celebrated their **TVOICYR** by eating cake. _____

13. Dan wanted to **HUEPRCSA** a new pair of boots. _____

14. I waited on the **MATEVPEN** outside the shop. _____

/ 7

15. We decided to **PEOMCTE** in the three-legged race. _____

16. The valley was popular due to its natural **TBEUYA**. _____

17. Olga has a strong **PINASOS** for looking after the planet. _____

18. My tallest sunflower was two metres in **GHTEHI**. _____

19. The criminal **MALCIED** he didn't carry out the robbery. _____

20. We had to **MTAESITE** the number of marbles in the jar. _____

/ 6

Section Three — Making Words

Word Ladders

Change one letter at a time to make the first word into the final word. The two answers must be real words.

Look at this example:

DATE (<u>HATE</u>) (<u>HATS</u>) HUTS

1. FOLD (_____) (_____) HOPE

2. VAST (_____) (_____) NEAT

3. RICH (_____) (_____) HIDE

4. BURN (_____) (_____) CARE

5. BOWL (_____) (_____) TOES

6. FILM (_____) (_____) PALE

7. NEWS (_____) (_____) VATS

Hint: At least one letter stays the same in the first and last words. Use these letters to help you work out the answers.

/ 7

8. CONE (_____) (_____) BEND

9. DIAL (_____) (_____) SEAM

10. FLOW (_____) (_____) CLAD

11. HARD (_____) (_____) HIDE

12. MENU (_____) (_____) BAND

13. WIFE (_____) (_____) MADE

14. YELP (_____) (_____) WALL

/ 7

15. GAIT (_____) (_____) VEIN

16. SHOES (_____) (_____) STEPS

17. STORM (_____) (_____) SHARK

18. RIVER (_____) (_____) WIDEN

19. PEACE (_____) (_____) COACH

20. DROVE (_____) (_____) GRAVY

/ 6

Closest Meaning

Underline two words, one from each set of brackets, that have the most similar meaning.

Look at this example:

(<u>run</u> swim dance)   (walk jump <u>sprint</u>)

Hint: Read all the words slowly several times to make sure you understand them properly.

1. (story novel book)   (poem tale article)

2. (attach combine merge)   (fasten multiply disconnect)

3. (chore hobby job)   (occupation employer leisure)

4. (chest stomach organ)   (body muscle tummy)

5. (vessel row sailing)   (ship cruise canal)

6. (performance scene audience)   (actor spectators stage)

7. (above beneath beside)   (opposite inside below)

/ 7

8. (summarise enquire criticise)   (conclude ask identify)

9. (safety refuge immunity)   (healthy welfare careful)

10. (feeble soft fragile)   (delicate slim sleek)

11. (excited rebellious chaotic)   (disaster savage disorderly)

12. (dispatched inflated elevated)   (transported raised submerged)

13. (abandoned isolated lonely)   (secluded solitude abnormal)

14. (component member category)   (summary description genre)

/ 7

15. (hidden illicit irrational)   (puzzling concealed cryptic)

16. (obedient alive conscious)   (aware ignorant energetic)

17. (accompany solider guard)   (protect defence attack)

18. (uncover research reveal)   (endeavour investigate interrogate)

19. (prejudice disrespect sympathy)   (tolerance vigour preconception)

20. (thoughtless blunt pointless)   (abrupt unexpected outrageous)

/ 6

Closest Meaning

Find the word that means the same, or nearly the same, as the word on the left. Underline your answer.

Look at this example:

stop   begin <u>halt</u> start go

1. **helpful**   essential loyal useful guidance

2. **touch**   taste feel grab secure

3. **globe**   shape sphere circle oval

4. **stay**   remain delay continue recur

5. **rinse**   wash drain bath soak

6. **insert**   place cover extract embed

7. **scratch**   itchy wound injury graze

Hint: Cross out any words that you think are definitely wrong as you go along.

/ 7

8. **patio**   garden terrace path balcony

9. **giggle**   cry wriggle chuckle wheeze

10. **knock**   fall thump tip stamp

11. **joyful**   amiable eager naive cheerful

12. **aroma**   air atmosphere scent murmur

13. **glance**   glimpse stare watch gaze

14. **drift**   travel wobble stray sway

/ 7

15. **habit**   characteristic custom personality obsession

16. **condemn**   threaten damage exclude criticise

17. **degrade**   ruin destroy humiliate provoke

18. **mannerism**   personality appearance trait tone

19. **writhe**   straighten squirm bend curl

20. **oscillate**   changing preserve fluctuate stabilise

/ 6

Closest Meaning

Complete the word on the right so that it means the same, or nearly the same, as the word on the left.

Look at this example:

fix [r][e][p][a][i][r]

1. **fabric**   [c][ ][ ][ ][h]

2. **whine**   [w][ ][ ][l]

3. **try**   [ ][t][ ][e][ ][p][ ]

4. **floor**   [g][ ][ ][u][ ][d]

5. **spin**   [ ][o][t][ ][ ][e]

6. **weary**   [t][ ][ ][e][ ]

7. **arrange**   [o][ ][g][ ][ ][ ][s][e]

Hint: If you're stuck, try looking in a thesaurus for words that mean the same — they're sometimes called 'synonyms'.

/ 7

8. **edge**   [b][ ][ ][d][e][ ]

9. **blurry**   [ ][a][z][ ]

10. **silence**   [ ][u][ ][ ][t]

11. **issue**   [ ][r][ ][ ][l][ ][m]

12. **danger**   [ ][a][z][a][ ][ ]

13. **gulp**   [ ][a][ ][l][ ][w]

14. **assured**   [c][ ][ ][f][ ][ ][ ][ ][t]

/ 7

15. **sorrow**   [m][ ][ ][ ][r][y]

16. **knowledge**   [ ][n][ ][ ][r][a][ ][ ][o][n]

17. **coach**   [ ][e][a][ ][h]

18. **map**   [ ][h][a][ ][ ]

19. **distraught**   [ ][i][s][ ][r][e][ ][ ][d]

20. **camouflage**   [ ][i][s][ ][u][ ][ ][ ]

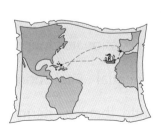

/ 6

 ✓   ✓   ✓

Section Four — Word Meanings

Opposite Meaning

Underline two words, one from each set of brackets, that have the most opposite meaning.

Look at this example:

(purchase <u>cheap</u> free)   (<u>expensive</u> money bargain)

1. (remember memory think)   (ponder recall forget)

2. (dense agile distant)   (nimble slow heavy)

3. (surface brittle rough)   (bumpy smooth texture)

4. (student scholar experienced)   (practice professional amateur)

5. (intelligent thriving sizeable)   (failing successful positive)

6. (neglectful regretful careful)   (cheerful afflicted attentive)

7. (sensitive boisterous gentle)   (restrained chatty warm)

Hint: If you don't recognise a word, look it up in a dictionary.

/ 7

8. (invent stifle burden)   (suppress repress allow)

9. (relieve reserve indulge)   (deprive treat luxury)

10. (sentimental affection caring)   (warmth dislike endearing)

11. (escape gather disperse)   (accumulate flee increase)

12. (divulge discover expand)   (prohibit withhold repel)

13. (control composed nervous)   (agitated careful wistful)

14. (forlorn earnest serious)   (pensive regretful hopeful)

/ 7

15. (dubious definite distinct)   (believable specific qualified)

16. (compassionate touching avid)   (disrespectful ignorant uncaring)

17. (influential vital dominant)   (inessential imperative undesirable)

18. (gentle benign harmful)   (scary painful malignant)

19. (disorder submissive daunted)   (persistent rebellious mischievous)

20. (peaceful harmony melody)   (difference discord disaster)

/ 6

Section Four — Word Meanings

Opposite Meaning

Find the word that means the opposite, or nearly the opposite, of the word on the left. Underline your answer.

Look at this example:

large   big enormous giant <u>small</u>

Hint: If you're stuck, try looking in a thesaurus for words that mean the opposite.

1. **leave**   scramble flutter skid linger

2. **smug**   humble complacent optimistic egotistical

3. **remote**   separate secluded close isolated

4. **repugnant**   caring inviting selfless effortless

5. **gloomy**   dire bright matte ornate

6. **firm**   subtle scarce active uncertain

7. **contract**   prolong tighten shrivel swell

/ 7

8. **miserable**   gracious jovial pessimistic considerate

9. **drab**   dreary modest flamboyant plain

10. **disobey**   spread adhere flout facilitate

11. **trusting**   naive nervous cynical discontented

12. **objective**   impartial biased inquisitive desire

13. **agreeable**   compelling strict concordant contrary

14. **devious**   deceitful shy sincere unreasonable

/ 7

15. **feisty**   brazen secretive timid courageous

16. **unconcerned** reckless furious restrained anxious

17. **claim**   approve overlook retain waive

18. **adept**   complicated proficient adequate inept

19. **predictable** capricious endless optional frantic

20. **indefinite** imprecise beneficial unequivocal questionable

/ 6

Section Four — Word Meanings

Opposite Meaning

Complete the word on the right so that it means the opposite, or nearly the opposite, of the word on the left.

Look at this example:

shut   o p e n

1. **solid**   f ☐ u ☐ d

2. **dangerous**   ☐ ☐ f ☐

3. **maximum**   ☐ i ☐ ☐ ☐ m

4. **watch**   ☐ ☐ n o ☐ e

5. **interior**   ☐ ☐ t ☐ ☐ ☐ r

6. **float**   ☐ ☐ ☐ k

7. **widespread** u n ☐ m ☐ o ☐

> **Hint:** Make sure you check the spelling of your answer carefully — it's easy to muddle up letters when you're not writing the whole word out.

/ 7

8. **same**   ☐ ☐ ☐ f ☐ ☐ e n ☐

9. **organised**   ☐ ☐ s ☐ y

10. **broad**   ☐ ☐ r r ☐ ☐

11. **cloudy**   ☐ ☐ ☐ n y

12. **climb**   ☐ ☐ s c ☐ ☐ ☐

13. **authentic** ☐ ☐ k ☐

14. **present**   ☐ ☐ s e ☐ ☐

/ 7

15. **lazy**   ☐ n e ☐ g ☐ t ☐ ☐

16. **agree**   ☐ ☐ j e ☐ ☐

17. **meticulous** c ☐ ☐ e l ☐ s ☐

18. **famous**   ☐ n ☐ ☐ o w ☐

19. **vulnerable** ☐ r ☐ t ☐ c ☐ e d

20. **correct**   e ☐ ☐ ☐ n ☐ ☐ u s

/ 6

Multiple Meanings

Choose the word that has a similar meaning to the words in both sets of brackets. Underline your answer.

Look at this example:

(travel move) (turn try)   effort advance attempt <u>go</u>

Hint: If you're sure a word isn't correct, cross it out, e.g. e̶f̶f̶o̶r̶t̶.

1. (tolerant lenient)   (sufferer invalid)   victim passive patient willing

2. (bright sunny)   (airy weightless)   frail shiny dainty light

3. (disgust repulse)   (uprising mutiny)   rebellion repel outrage revolt

4. (border outline)   (advantage lead)   edge boundary fringe position

5. (calm settle)   (devise produce)   invent design soothe compose

6. (baffle confuse)   (fling toss)   upset throw launch fluster

/ 6

7. (clean wipe)   (sprinkle powder)   spray drench distribute dust

8. (business enterprise)   (visitors guests)   society company customers crowd

9. (disregard neglect)   (view survey)   omit scan overlook consider

10. (ornament headdress)   (top peak)   brow crown summit tip

11. (question interrogate)   (heat cook)   grill stew boil scald

12. (loose baggy)   (lax careless)   limp slack droopy sluggish

/ 6

13. (fasten secure)   (fold collapse)   warp crease join give buckle

14. (tone ambience)   (air sky)   scene spirit atmosphere essence cloud

15. (suppose suspect)   (take gain)   guess imagine sense assume possess

16. (warm balmy)   (gentle tame)   mild calm docile delicate kind

17. (angle bend)   (trap enclose)   crook corner hoax bait curve

18. (flare flicker)   (initiate inspire)   kindle dart electrify jolt spark

/ 6

Section Four — Word Meanings

Odd One Out

Three of the words in each list are linked. Underline the word that is not related to these three.

Look at this example:

easy   simple   basic   <u>difficult</u>

1. professor   student   teacher   instructor

2. church   chapel   congregation   cathedral

3. camel   cactus   sand   dry

4. crave   need   desire   want

5. coal   petrol   wood   fire

6. ascend   dive   plunge   plummet

7. star   moon   rocket   planet

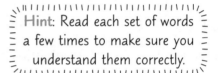
Hint: Read each set of words a few times to make sure you understand them correctly.

/ 7

8. modern   current   original   contemporary

9. surround   conceal   enclose   encompass

10. obtain   release   seize   capture

11. theory   belief   method   hypothesis

12. sudden   abrupt   surprising   immediate

13. clone   duplicate   revive   imitate

14. divide   separate   disconnect   incorporate

/ 7

15. grumpy   irritable   moody   pensive

16. guess   answer   predict   forecast

17. topple   trip   tremble   tumble

18. grating   unwanted   annoying   irksome

19. compelling   absorbing   captivating   imposing

20. creative   inventive   intuitive   artistic

/ 6

Odd Ones Out

Three of the words in each list are linked. Underline the two words that are not related to these three.

Look at this example:

loud   noisy   <u>quiet</u>   rowdy   <u>peaceful</u>

1. walk   stroll   run   jog   sprint

2. city   location   area   town   place

3. cotton   silk   steel   wool   brass

4. hasty   quick   rapid   lively   active

5. dawn   sundown   morning   dusk   daybreak

6. soil   root   bark   leaf   water

7. fix   pin   nail   tools   screw

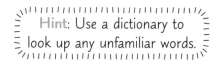

Hint: Use a dictionary to look up any unfamiliar words.

 / 7

8. money   token   cash   coupon   voucher

9. dodge   avoid   roam   wander   escape

10. coast   lake   shore   bank   river

11. adjust   enlarge   improve   swell   grow

12. appearance   personality   character   disposition   expression

13. distance   ruler   thermometer   temperature   compass

/ 7

14. comma   letter   asterisk   apostrophe   font

15. solution   impression   understanding   interpretation   recognition

16. triumph   overshoot   succeed   win   exceed

17. ministry   regulation   policy   government   law

18. destroy   deplete   wreck   diminish   devastate

19. back   develop   recommend   approve   upgrade

/ 6

20. obvious   evident   notable   apparent   obscure

Section Four — Word Meanings

Word Connections

Choose two words, one from each set of brackets, that complete the sentence in the most sensible way. Underline both words.

Look at this example:

Eye is to (face blink <u>see</u>) as **mouth** is to (<u>taste</u> tongue lips).

Hint: Understanding the difference between nouns, verbs and adjectives should help you with these questions.

1. **Umbrella** is to (rain shelter wet) as **cap** is to (sun helmet head).

2. **Lime** is to (green sour citrus) as **watermelon** is to (crunchy seeds sweet).

3. **Wave** is to (greet hand friendly) as **wink** is to (eye twitch flutter).

4. **Basketball** is to (bounce score hoop) as **football** is to (boots defend goal).

5. **Vase** is to (ornament flower delicate) as **pan** is to (kitchen soup handle).

6. **Sailor** is to (sea oar ship) as **pilot** is to (fly plane captain).

7. **Needle** is to (sharp tapestry sew) as **trowel** is to (dig outside spade).

/ 7

8. **Pigeon** is to (wood eggs fly) as **penguin** is to (freezing waddle wings).

9. **Meagre** is to (weak insufficient unable) as **considerable** is to (large serious strong).

10. **Test** is to (assessment mark progress) as **survey** is to (participants poll interrogate).

11. **Bread** is to (slice loaf granary) as **milk** is to (pour dairy liquid).

12. **Mischievous** is to (naughty mysterious immature) as **courteous** is to (shy timid polite).

13. **Architect** is to (draw pencil buildings) as **dentist** is to (food teeth hygienic).

14. **Impulsive** is to (boring planned gentle) as **humble** is to (vain loud rude).

/ 7

15. **Strict** is to (stern unkind terrible) as **lenient** is to (forgiving friendly affectionate).

16. **Words** are to (dictionary speech rhyme) as **recipes** are to (taste cookbook ingredients).

17. **Hope** is to (positive long achieve) as **doubt** is to (ambiguous question difficult).

18. **Hotel** is to (stay accommodation rent) as **supermarket** is to (till food trolley).

19. **Offend** is to (insult flatter enrage) as **assist** is to (amiable rude hinder).

/ 6

20. **Office** is to (stationery colleagues work) as **school** is to (bus learn assembly).

Reorder Words to Make a Sentence

Find the two words that should be swapped in order for each sentence to make sense. Underline both words.

Look at this example:

My <u>is</u> ice cream flavour <u>favourite</u> strawberry.

1. Rebecca with to the cinema went some friends.

2. The squirrel up quickly scurried the tree trunk.

3. I discovered an old photograph box that in.

4. It was extremely windy today the house outside.

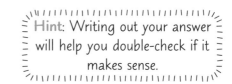

Hint: Writing out your answer will help you double-check if it makes sense.

5. We went to local some alpacas at the visit farm.

6. I baked my Victoria sponge cake for a parents.

7. The travel method of transport is to fastest by plane.

/ 7

8. We celebrate my friend's birthday, to had a jungle-themed party.

9. The museum of fossils at the collection is amazing.

10. I am going later with my family camping this year.

11. I last to write a fantasy novel started week.

12. We built sandcastles to day when we went all the beach.

13. Are favourite flowers are tulips because they our colourful.

14. Sheep farmer now has fifty-two the in the field.

/ 7

15. Pineapple on my favourite topping to put is pizza.

16. On Halloween, I dressed up as a pumpkin orange bright.

17. There delicately three goldfinches perched were on the branch.

18. Erupted loud and powerful roar a from the lion's mouth.

19. I found a deep sigh of relief when I breathed my homework down the sofa.

/ 6

20. I was the average person in my class but now I'm tallest height.

Section Four — Word Meanings

Reorder Words to Make a Sentence

Rearrange the words so that each sentence makes sense.
Underline the word which doesn't fit into the sentence.

Look at this example:

> the morning get I up <u>bed</u> early in

The remaining words can be arranged into the sentence:
I get up early in the morning.

1. floor it slithered the slowly snake the across

2. pirate's the on where parrot the sat shoulder

3. with rounders I my today now friends played

4. evening night to stargazing go likes she at

5. autumn in leaves the brown turn seasons the

6. is than brother my three me older years age

Hint: Try writing out what you think the answer should be to see if your sentence works.

/ 6

7. own would to pet like I a rabbit wanted

8. has he cereal for meal and breakfast banana a

9. on to seaside we went holiday going the are

10. drama look yesterday forward to club going to I really

11. was my looked teacher the that homework relieved gave done

12. with oranges a salad made we fruit and lots strawberries

/ 6

13. are my respect enjoying kind they very friends I because

14. every rehearsing am school for night play act I our

15. found giraffe leaf a chewed and hungry the eat it

16. next street there a on that is cat our lives

17. for the won most correctly I an spelling award words because

18. determined the that learnt violin she perform was to song on

/ 6

Section Four — Word Meanings

Complete the Sum

Find the missing number to complete each sum.
Write your answer on the line.

Look at this example:

$$5 + 7 = 6 \times (\underline{\,2\,})$$

1. $3 \times 6 = 24 - (\underline{})$

2. $15 \div 3 = 10 - (\underline{})$

3. $8 \times 3 = 15 + (\underline{})$

4. $16 \div 4 = 13 - (\underline{})$

5. $5 \times 4 - 6 = 7 + (\underline{})$

6. $10 \div 2 + 3 = 13 - (\underline{})$

7. $7 \times 3 - 4 = 6 + (\underline{})$

/ 7

8. $9 \div 3 + 7 = 4 + (\underline{})$

9. $6 \times 4 - 15 = 3 \times (\underline{})$

10. $3 \times 6 \div 2 = 14 - (\underline{})$

11. $27 \div 3 - 4 = 25 \div (\underline{})$

12. $3 \times 8 - 4 = 4 \times (\underline{})$

13. $12 \div 3 + 4 = 16 \div (\underline{})$

14. $21 \div 3 - 4 = 11 - (\underline{})$

/ 7

15. $4 \times 3 \div 2 = 2 + 8 - (\underline{})$

16. $8 \div 2 + 9 - 3 = 5 \times (\underline{})$

17. $20 \div 4 \times 8 - 10 = 3 \times (\underline{})$

18. $9 \times 2 + 4 = 8 \times 2 + (\underline{})$

19. $14 \div 2 \times 3 + 5 = 2 \times (\underline{})$

20. $36 \div 6 + 8 - 11 = 18 \div 2 - (\underline{})$

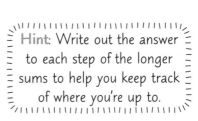

Hint: Write out the answer to each step of the longer sums to help you keep track of where you're up to.

/ 6

Letter Sequences

Find the pair of letters that continues each sequence in the best way. Use the alphabet to help you.

A B C D E F G H I J K L M N O P Q R S T U V W X Y Z

Look at this example:

| AB | BC | CD | DE | EF | (<u>FG</u>) |

1. OO   NP   MQ   LR   KS   (____)

2. JQ   LO   NM   PK   RI   (____)

3. BZ   CV   ER   FN   HJ   (____)

4. SN   PK   NI   KF   ID   (____)

5. SN   QO   OQ   MR   KT   (____)

6. BP   EN   EM   HK   HJ   (____)

7. GC   DD   AD   XE   UE   (____)

Hint: Make a note of the pattern each letter is following to help you work out the next letter.

/ 7

8. JR   KP   IO   JO   HP   (____)

9. IC   GD   EF   CI   AM   (____)

10. BD   CF   EC   HE   LB   (____)

11. DV   CU   CS   DP   FL   (____)

12. DR   DU   CA   AD   XJ   (____)

13. GM   JO   HL   KN   IK   (____)

14. QN   PK   PI   QH   SH   (____)

/ 7

15. PW   RU   ST   ST   RU   (____)

16. NC   PA   TZ   VX   ZW   (____)

17. HD   KC   IA   LX   JT   (____)

18. LP   MR   MU   LY   JD   (____)

19. EE   HD   ID   LE   MG   (____)

20. KN   JS   HW   EZ   AB   (____)

/ 6

Section Five — Maths and Sequences

Number Sequences

Find the number that continues each sequence in the best way.
Write your answer on the line.

Look at this example:

3   5   7   9   11   (_13_)

1. **1   4   7   10   13**   (____)

2. **35   29   23   17   11**   (____)

3. **11   23   35   47   59**   (____)

4. **64   32   16   8   4**   (____)

5. **3   4   6   9   13**   (____)

6. **4   9   16   25   36**   (____)

7. **2   16   4   8   8   4**   (____)

Hint: There could be two different patterns in a single sequence — if you're stuck, see if you can spot a pattern in alternating numbers.

/ 7

8. **15   14   12   9   5**   (____)

9. **40   39   37   33   25**   (____)

10. **3   3   6   9   15**   (____)

11. **56   48   59   46   62   44**   (____)

12. **6   10   19   35   60**   (____)

13. **2   9   5   18   8   36**   (____)

14. **10   11   11   10   8**   (____)

/ 7

15. **39   38   36   32   24**   (____)

16. **100   75   59   50   46**   (____)

17. **1   3   6   11   18**   (____)

18. **6   8   12   4   24   2**   (____)

19. **480   240   80   20**   (____)

20. **1   2   3   6   9   18**   (____)

Hint: Some sequences might use prime numbers or square numbers, so make sure you know them.

/ 6

Section Five — Maths and Sequences

Related Numbers

Find the number that completes the final set of numbers in the same way as the first two sets. Write your answer on the line.

Look at this example:

1 (3) 5   12 (14) 16   8 (_10_) 12

1. 5 (7) 2   4 (9) 5   3 (____) 4

2. 10 (5) 2   8 (2) 4   18 (____) 6

3. 9 (6) 3   8 (6) 2   10 (____) 3

4. 6 (11) 16   6 (9) 12   8 (____) 14

5. 4 (12) 3   5 (15) 3   2 (____) 4

6. 5 (9) 14   3 (8) 11   7 (____) 16

7. 3 (4) 2   4 (9) 6   7 (____) 7

/ 7

8.   11 (14) 17   39 (29) 19   19 (____) 27

9.   2 (14) 28   4 (8) 32   3 (____) 27

10. 6 (37) 6   7 (36) 5   4 (____) 6

11. 3 (18) 12   5 (15) 6   4 (____) 8

12. 19 (5) 9   16 (4) 8   11 (____) 7

13. 5 (24) 4   6 (35) 5   8 (____) 3

14. 24 (6) 12   20 (12) 5   12 (____) 4

/ 7

15. 7 (30) 4   5 (27) 5   6 (____) 3

16. 27 (10) 3   35 (8) 5   28 (____) 4

17. 6 (8) 4   9 (6) 2   6 (____) 6

18. 5 (5) 10   3 (9) 18   2 (____) 14

19. 2 (10) 7   5 (26) 6   4 (____) 8

/ 6

20. 3 (3) 3   5 (17) 11   8 (____) 10

Letter-Coded Sums

Each letter stands for a number. Work out the answer to each sum as a letter. Write your answer on the line.

Look at this example:

A = 2   B = 3   C = 4   D = 6   E = 8   E ÷ A = (_C_)

1. A = 1   B = 3   C = 5   D = 6   E = 8   B + C = (___)

2. A = 2   B = 3   C = 5   D = 7   E = 10   E – B = (___)

3. A = 2   B = 4   C = 6   D = 10   E = 12   A × C = (___)

4. A = 2   B = 4   C = 6   D = 8   E = 10   D – C + A = (___)

5. A = 3   B = 5   C = 9   D = 15   E = 17   A + D – C = (___)

/ 5

Hint: Work out the answer as a number first, then work out which letter matches that number.

6. A = 2   B = 3   C = 4   D = 6   E = 22   B × C ÷ D = (___)

7. A = 2   B = 3   C = 9   D = 14   E = 24   B × C – B = (___)

8. A = 4   B = 7   C = 8   D = 12   E = 28   E ÷ B + A = (___)

9. A = 2   B = 4   C = 9   D = 15   E = 20   E – D + B = (___)

10. A = 3   B = 6   C = 9   D = 12   E = 13   D ÷ A + C = (___)

11. A = 1   B = 3   C = 7   D = 11   E = 21   B × C ÷ E = (___)

/ 6

12. A = 2   B = 4   C = 12   D = 19   E = 28   E ÷ B × A – A = (___)

13. A = 2   B = 7   C = 9   D = 16   E = 30   D × A – C + B = (___)

14. A = 2   B = 4   C = 6   D = 8   E = 20   C × D ÷ B – D = (___)

15. A = 4   B = 8   C = 11   D = 12   E = 32   E ÷ B × C – E = (___)

16. A = 3   B = 5   C = 6   D = 12   E = 18   A × D ÷ E + C – B = (___)

/ 5

Section Five — Maths and Sequences

Letter Connections

Mark the pair of letters that completes each sentence in the most sensible way. Use the alphabet to help you.

A B C D E F G H I J K L M N O P Q R S T U V W X Y Z

Look at this example:

BG is to **EJ** as **KP** is to (OS   NT   <u>NS</u>   LO   MR).

1. **PQ** is to **RS** as **FG** is to   (DE   HI   HJ   GI   ID).

2. **CX** is to **DW** as **SH** is to   (IR   TF   TG   UG   UF).

3. **JI** is to **FE** as **RQ** is to   (MN   ON   NM   PO   NP).

4. **BC** is to **LM** as **OP** is to   (YX   ZA   WX   WY   YZ).

5. **AD** is to **HK** as **IL** is to   (OS   PR   NR   PS   QS).

6. **KM** is to **EG** as **VX** is to   (PR   NO   SQ   SP   PQ).

7. **HR** is to **EW** as **DN** is to   (AR   AS   BS   FR   ZS).

> **Hint:** Check for mirror pairs, where the letters are an equal distance from the centre of the alphabet — so N is a mirror of M, O is a mirror of L and so on.

/ 7

8. **SH** is to **VE** as **JQ** is to   (NM   ML   MN   WD   QJ).

9. **LH** is to **GC** as **YU** is to   (UP   TO   UO   SN   TP).

10. **FU** is to **BY** as **LO** is to   (HS   GT   HT   SH   IR).

11. **IU** is to **SO** as **OT** is to   (ZO   YN   YM   XN   ZM).

12. **PK** is to **UF** as **BY** is to   (YB   GT   HS   GU   TG).

13. **NJ** is to **EM** as **FP** is to   (WT   XS   SH   WS   TS).

14. **JL** is to **QO** as **AC** is to   (XY   XZ   ZX   YB   YW).

/ 7

15. **OS** is to **RM** as **MF** is to   (PZ   OY   QA   PY   QZ).

16. **IN** is to **RM** as **YH** is to   (SB   XC   BA   BS   XT).

17. **ZA** is to **SH** as **VE** is to   (MN   LO   NM   OL   OM).

18. **CM** is to **NG** as **FL** is to   (QE   QF   FP   RG   RF).

19. **TW** is to **DG** as **EM** is to   (VN   ND   NV   NF   VL).

20. **UB** is to **YF** as **JP** is to   (PJ   PK   QK   KP   KQ).

/ 6

Letter-Word Codes

Each question uses a different code. Use the alphabet to help you work out the answer to each question.

A B C D E F G H I J K L M N O P Q R S T U V W X Y Z

Look at this example:

If the code for **ZIP** is **YHO**, what is the code for **RUN**? __QTM__

Hint: Remember to look for mirror codes before you begin your working out.

1. If the code for **PET** is **RGV**, what is the code for **SUN**? _____

2. If the code for **CAP** is **XZK**, what is **YZM** the code for? _____

3. If the code for **SEEM** is **PBBJ**, what is **ELOK** the code for? _____

4. If the code for **GRIN** is **TIRM**, what is **IZGV** the code for? _____

5. If the code for **COWS** is **DNXR**, what is the code for **THIS**? _____

/ 5

6. If the code for **HELP** is **FFJQ**, what is **UJLE** the code for? _____

7. If the code for **MATCH** is **NZGXS**, what is **RMWVC** the code for? _____

8. If the code for **REAL** is **THCO**, what is the code for **DUCK**? _____

9. If the code for **FLICK** is **UORXP**, what is **TRZMG** the code for? _____

10. If the code for **OUT** is **PWW**, what is **ICP** the code for? _____

/ 5

11. If the code for **BOARD** is **YLZIW**, what is **UFWTV** the code for? _____

12. If the code for **SMILE** is **SLGIA**, what is **BQGKC** the code for? _____

13. If the code for **MOUSE** is **KOWWK**, what is the code for **PLANT**? _____

14. If the code for **COAT** is **XLZG**, what is **YVZMH** the code for? _____

15. If the code for **SCARE** is **QBASG**, what is **PNUOF** the code for? _____

/ 5

Section Six — Logic and Coding

Number-Word Codes

The number codes for throo of these four words are listed in a random order.
Work out the code to answer the questions.

Hint: Look for patterns in the codes, such as double letters, to help you break them.

HOOD   **LOSS**   **SOUL**   **LOUD**

3625   1664   5633

1. Find the code for the word **LOUD**.   _____

2. Find the code for the word **HOLD**.   _____

3. Find the word that has the number code **5231**.   _____

/ 3

PLAY   **PREY**   **REAP**   **YELP**

1462   2651   3452

4. Find the code for the word **PLAY**.   _____

5. Find the code for the word **RELY**.   _____

6. Find the word that has the number code **1453**.   _____

/ 3

BIND   **DINE**   **BEND**   **HIDE**

6245   1246   3265

7. Find the code for the word **BEND**.   _____

8. Find the code for the word **HEED**.   _____

9. Find the word that has the number code **3246**.   _____

/ 3

ROTA   **DRAW**   **WART**   **TOAD**

1564   6345   2651

10. Find the code for the word **TOAD**.   _____

11. Find the code for the word **WORD**.   _____

12. Find the word that has the number code **6352**.   _____

/ 3

Section Six — Logic and Coding

Number-Word Codes

The number codes for three of these four words are listed in a random order.
Work out the code to answer the questions.

Hint: Write out your numbers and letters neatly as you work them out so that you don't get them confused.

TOMB   **BOAT**   **ATOM**   **COMA**

1432   **5321**   **4326**

13. Find the code for the word **COMA**.   _____

14. Find the code for the word **MOAT**.   _____

15. Find the word that has the number code **4153**.   _____

/ 3

MERE   **REAM**   **MUTE**   **TRAM**

1324   **2561**   **5461**

16. Find the code for the word **MERE**.   _____

17. Find the code for the word **TERM**.   _____

18. Find the word that has the number code **2534**.   _____

/ 3

DOSE   **SEND**   **ONCE**   **NODS**

3546   **6235**   **2415**

19. Find the code for the word **ONCE**.   _____

20. Find the code for the word **CODE**.   _____

21. Find the word that has the number code **5463**.   _____

/ 3

DARE   **RAGE**   **RANG**   **EARN**

4163   **3165**   **6152**

22. Find the code for the word **RAGE**.   _____

23. Find the code for the word **REND**.   _____

24. Find the word that has the number code **2316**.   _____

/ 3

Section Six — Logic and Coding

Word Grids

Use the words to fill in the blanks in the word grids. You must use all the words. One letter on each grid has been filled in for you.

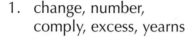 Hint: Use a pencil to write the words so you can rub out your workings if you make a mistake.

1. change, number, comply, excess, yearns

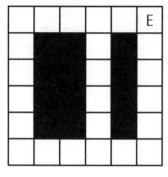

2. random, record, mirror, career, differ

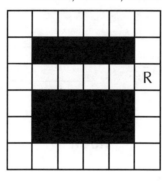

3. output, proper, nearby, treaty, option, throne

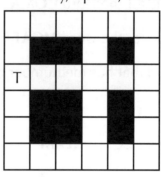

/ 3

4. grassy, inside, retain, regime, trails, malady

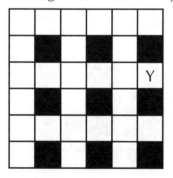

5. permit, border, letter, framed, hoarse, forego

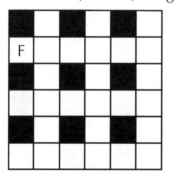

6. yonder, burden, memory, equine, entire, ordain

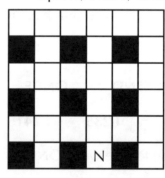

/ 3

7. impact, titled, fended, direct, immune, elated

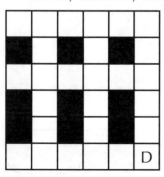

8. subdue, critic, crease, custom, orbits, imbibe

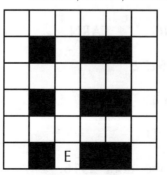

9. rarity, niggle, eatery, dinner, dilute, linger

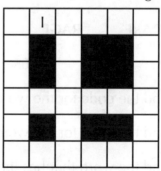

/ 3

Section Six — Logic and Coding

Using Rules of English

> Underline the most appropriate word from the brackets to complete each sentence. For example:
>
> Our pet rabbit Pip (**is   has   <u>will</u>   are**) turn two next week.

Hint: Try reading the words out loud to work out which word sounds like it belongs in the sentence.

1. I (**wants   will   want   wanting**) to paint my room yellow because I love bright colours.

2. My dad asks me to do my homework as soon as I (**got   get   getting   go**) in from school.

3. Oliver has been learning to swim (**since   when   though   while**) he was three years old.

4. We wanted to go to the circus even (**despite   though   still   although**) it was raining.

5. I (**liken   liking   like   likes**) visiting my grandparents at the weekend.

6. Ava had (**makes   making   make   made**) a friendship bracelet for Emily.

/ 6

7. They are going to watch a film on (**both   either   also   neither**) Friday or Saturday.

8. We tried to make flapjacks last night, (**but   if   instead   unless**) we forgot to add the syrup.

9. I (**see   saw   seeing   seen**) an old-fashioned steam train with my brother today.

10. It is (**near   like   mostly   only**) six weeks until the summer holidays begin.

11. I (**wave   waving   waves   waved**) happily at the postman as he walked past.

12. Rosie and (**me   I   my   mine**) have been friends since we were five.

/ 6

13. Sibi will (**shows   show   showed   shown**) us his card tricks at lunchtime tomorrow.

14. When Freya (**reclined   lounges   lied   sits**) on the sofa, she started to fall asleep.

15. The sheep bounced (**joy   joyful   joyfully   joyous**) across the field.

16. Amir (**score   scores   scoring   scored**) three goals during the football match yesterday.

17. Leila (**could   shall   must   will**) smell the pizza whilst it cooked in the oven.

18. I (**done   do   did   doing**) my best on the spelling test earlier this week.

/ 6

Choose a Word

Choose the correct words to complete each passage below.

Barn owls are nocturnal animals, which
1. ☐ meant
☐ mean
☐ means
they usually appear at night. What

makes them
2. ☐ unlike
☐ similar
☐ different
other species of bird is
3. ☐ there
☐ their
☐ they're
distinctive heart-shaped

faces. They
4. ☐ can
☐ are
☐ should
found on every
5. ☐ city
☐ country
☐ continent
in the world, except Antarctica.

/ 5

When my family and I go to the beach, I
6. ☐ investigate
☐ search
☐ examine
for the rarest shell I
7. ☐ can
☐ will
☐ could
find.

To have the best chance of
8. ☐ exhibiting
☐ designing
☐ discovering
a new shell, I make sure we go as
9. ☐ late
☐ soon
☐ recently

as possible after high tide,
10. ☐ before
☐ after
☐ whilst
anyone else has had time to comb the beach.

/ 5

Built in AD 122 by the Romans, Hadrian's Wall
11. ☐ escalated
☐ extended
☐ intensified
for 73 miles. Mainly

constructed from stone, the wall
12. ☐ took
☐ taken
☐ takes
around six years to build
13. ☐ though
☐ but
☐ and
was

up to six metres high. There were forts
14. ☐ protruded
☐ embedded
☐ assigned
into the wall, which
15. ☐ housed
☐ housing
☐ house

hundreds of soldiers at a time.

/ 5

Section Seven — Completing Passages

Choose a Word

Choose the correct words to complete each passage below.

At the weekend, I
16. ☐ gone
☐ going
☐ went
☐ visited
to a tropical butterfly house
17. ☐ along
☐ among
☐ with
☐ by
my friend Ahmad. It

was Ahmad's idea to go, as he used to
18. ☐ loathe
☐ enjoy
☐ prefer
☐ accept
going with his family and would sketch his

19. ☐ favoured
☐ favourite
☐ favouring
☐ favour
species in a notebook. We saw a
20. ☐ outstanding
☐ magnificent
☐ extensive
☐ medley
array of butterflies whilst

we were there. The finest, in my
21. ☐ opinion
☐ belief
☐ decision
☐ point
, was the Ulysses butterfly — it was the most

/ 6

vibrant shade of blue.

Located
22. ☐ near
☐ close
☐ just
☐ far
the northeastern coast
23. ☐ from
☐ on
☐ of
☐ with
Australia, the Great Barrier Reef is the

biggest coral reef ecosystem in the world. Although it
24. ☐ highlights
☐ attributes
☐ repeats
☐ resembles
a plant, coral is in fact a

marine animal. One of the many
25. ☐ disadvantages
☐ difficulties
☐ benefits
☐ confirmations
of coral reef ecosystems
26. ☐ combines
☐ includes
☐ reveals
☐ introduces

their ability to protect shores from storms. This is something that is
27. ☐ defended
☐ delivered
☐ saved
☐ threatened
by the rising

temperatures associated with climate change, which can damage the coral.

/ 6

Section Seven — Completing Passages

Fill in Missing Letters

Fill in the missing letters to complete the words in the following passages.

1. Standing elegantly in the c☐r☐er of my grandparents' garden is a majestic apple tree

2. with a bountiful supply of bright green apples. G☐☐☐ing up, we would wander to

3. the b☐t☐☐m of the garden and fill a wicker basket to the brim, almost making the

4. basket too heavy to carry. My grandma would then bake a d☐☐i☐ious apple

5. crumble, with me and my brother e☐g☐☐ly awaiting the moment the timer went off.

6. Years later, I still get n☐☐t☐lgic for the sweet smell of caramelising apples

7. waft☐☐☐ from the oven.

/ 7

8. Between about 1300 and 1850, global t☐mp☐r☐tures were significantly colder

9. than they are t☐☐☐y . This period in time is referred to as "The Little Ice Age".

10. Sometimes it got so cold that the River Thames, in London, completely f☐☐z☐ .

11. In the winter of 1607-1608, in an act of ing☐n☐☐ty , Londoners decided to profit

12. from a challenging situation by setting up the first Frost Fairs. A di☐e☐☐e range

13. of sights could be seen, from food stalls to f☐☐t☐all pitches. It would have

14. been an extr☐or☐☐nary sight to behold.

/ 7

15. Earth's moon is the closest object you can see in the sky at n☐☐☐t . This celestial

16. body has a distinctive pitted appearance as a re☐☐lt of numerous asteroids and

17. meteorites colliding with its s☐☐f☐ce . The Moon's gravity plays a

18. cr☐t☐☐al role in controlling Earth's ocean tides. A total of twelve people

19. have st☐☐☐ed foot on the Moon since 1969. To date, no evidence has been

20. found to suggest life exists on the Moon. However, ex☐☐☐rations and

21. research are ongoing to de☐☐☐mine whether life exists there.

/ 7

Fill in Missing Letters

Fill in the missing letters to complete the words in the following passages.

22. Ada Lovelace was a British mathematician with an in[   ]st in machinery, who is

23. credited as the founder of c[   ]p[   ]er programming. Born in 1815, Lovelace

24. later bef[   ]i[   ]ded a fellow mathematician, Charles Babbage, who she

25. worked and shared ideas with. She made the realisation that mac[   ]es

26. could be used to perform co[   ]x mathematical functions. Her pioneering work

27. is commemorated on Lovelace Day, every O[   ]er , when other

28. influential sc[   ]n[   ]fic achievements made by women are recognised.

/ 7

29. Snowflakes l[   ]d[   ]d gently on Lola's smiling face as she glanced up at the vast

30. expanse of sky, which was a sea of white. The ground b[   ]ne[   ]h her was blanketed

31. with pristine snow, and as she looked around her, she felt an overwhelming se[   ]s[   ] of

32. admiration for this beautiful winter m[   ]n[   ]g . Never before had she felt so in

33. awe of the magic and beauty of nature. The gl[   ]ning landscape was so

34. un[   ]st[   ]bed, it felt like a dream. Tentatively, she placed one foot in

35. front of the other, re[   ]sh[   ]ng the sound of the muffled crunch below.

/ 7

36. Situated in n[   ]th[   ]rn India, the Taj Mahal was built by Mughal Emperor Shah Jahan

37. between 1631 and 1648. Constructed alongside the river Yamuna, in an en[   ]ous

38. garden, it was commissioned in m[   ]m[   ]y of the Emperor's late wife, who died

39. in childbirth. The vast mausoleum is built from white marble and is d[   ]co[   ]ted

40. with a variety of semi-precious stones. Reaching an impr[   ]ive height of 73 metres,

41. it f[   ]ures an awe-inspiring central dome, which is a distinguishing

42. characteristic of this universally re[   ]g[   ]sed building.

/ 7

Section Seven — Completing Passages

Section Eight — Comprehension

Finding Hidden Facts

Read the information carefully, then use it to answer the question that follows. Write your answer on the line.

Hint: To keep track of the information you're given, it's a good idea to make a tally chart for each question.

1. Mila, Leo, Karim, Bella and Aisha are discussing the animals they've seen in their garden.

    Mila and Aisha have both seen a squirrel. Everyone has seen a bee. Aisha is the only child who has seen a hedgehog. The only one not to have seen a butterfly is Mila. Everyone except Karim has seen a sparrow.

    Who has seen the **most** animals in their garden? _____

    / 1

2. Amber, Eva, Finn, Zachary and Noah all play different musical instruments.

    Eva, Zachary and Noah all play the drums. Everyone except Noah plays the guitar. Zachary is the only child who plays the clarinet. Finn and Noah both play the piano. The only one not to play the recorder is Amber.

    Who plays the **fewest** musical instruments? _____

    / 1

3. Ranj, Isla, Oscar, Ivy and Peter are each painting a picture.

    Peter is the only one who paints with the colour purple. Ranj and Ivy both use red. Only two children, Oscar and Peter, use orange. Everyone except Isla uses blue. The only one who uses pink is Oscar. Ranj, Ivy and Oscar all use green. Isla is the only child who uses yellow.

    Who uses the **most** colours in their painting? _____

    / 1

4. Jack, Ben, Sarita, Mary and Liam are talking about what's in their rucksacks.

    Sarita's rucksack is the only one with a ruler in it. Mary and Liam both have a notebook in theirs. Everyone except Ben has a pencil case in their rucksack. Jack has an apple and a banana in his. Mary is the only one who doesn't have a bottle in her rucksack.

    Who has the **fewest** belongings in their rucksack? _____

    / 1

Finding Hidden Facts

Read the information carefully, then use it to answer the question that follows. Write your answer on the line.

Hint: Keep an eye out for repeated information — make sure you don't count it twice!

5. Krish, Freddie, Lola, Sasha and Rupy visited a local farm.

    Freddie and Sasha both saw a cow and a pig. No one except Krish saw a horse.
    Everyone saw a chicken. The only one who spotted a sheep was Lola. Sasha is the only
    one who caught sight of a goat. Rupy saw a duck and a chicken. Lola and Krish are the
    only ones who saw an alpaca.

    Who saw the **fewest** animals on the farm? _____

    / 1

6. Mia, Poppy, Kaspar, Eliza and Louis are discussing what classes they have today.

    Mia is the only one who has German. Everyone except Eliza has English. Louis and
    Kaspar both have Geography and History. Eliza has Science and Art. Poppy has French
    and English. Only two children, Eliza and Mia, have Maths.

    Who has the **fewest** number of classes? _____

    / 1

7. Miryam, Lorenzo, George, Priya and Annette are all having vegetables with their dinner.

    Everyone except Lorenzo is having carrots. Annette is having broccoli and courgette.
    The only person who is having peas is Priya. Lorenzo's dinner is the only one to include
    cabbage. Miryam is having two different vegetables with her dinner.

    Who is having the **most** types of vegetable? _____

    / 1

8. Rupert, Lily, Tomasso, Amira and Matthew are making cakes for a bake sale.

    Rupert and Tomasso both make a victoria sponge. No one except Matthew bakes a
    ginger cake. Rupert is the only one to make a carrot cake. Everyone except Tomasso
    bakes a lemon drizzle. Rupert and Amira both make a chocolate cake. Everyone bakes
    a coffee cake except Rupert. Lily bakes a red velvet cake and a lemon drizzle.

    Who bakes the **most** cakes? _____

    / 1

Solve the Riddle

Read the information carefully, then use it to answer the question that follows. Underline the correct answer.

Hint: Make a note of the key pieces of information as you go along.

1. Charlie, Olga, Kai, Dev and Eve are comparing how many apples they picked. Kai picked four apples. Charlie picked fewer apples than Dev. Olga picked one fewer apple than Kai and two fewer apples than Eve. Dev didn't pick the most apples.

   Which one of the sentences below **must** be true?

   A Charlie picked seven apples.

   B Olga picked more apples than Dev.

   C Dev picked the fewest apples.

   D Eve picked the most apples.

/ 1

2. Elijah, Ava, Saira, Nick and Molly are each thinking of a number between 1 and 6. Ava is thinking of a number lower than 3. Elijah is thinking of an even number. Nick is the only person thinking of the number 1. The number Saira is thinking of is twice as big as Ava's.

   Which one of the sentences below **must** be true?

   A Saira is thinking of the number 4.

   B Elijah is thinking of the number 6.

   C Ava is thinking of an odd number.

   D Molly is thinking of the biggest number.

/ 1

3. Harriet, Pasha, Ria, Louise and Isaac all have their birthdays in the same week. Ria's birthday is on Saturday. Harriet's birthday is after Pasha's. Pasha's birthday is earlier in the week than Ria's. Louise's birthday is two days before Harriet's.

   Which one of the sentences below **cannot** be true?

   A Harriet and Ria have the same birthday.

   B Ria and Louise have the same birthday.

   C Pasha and Louise have the same birthday.

   D Isaac and Pasha have the same birthday.

/ 1

Solve the Riddle

Read the information carefully, then use it to answer the question that follows. Underline the correct answer.

4. Viv, Becky, Maria, Jake and Dan are all in the same class at school.
Dan is 125 cm tall. The shortest person is 120 cm tall. Jake is 2 cm taller than Dan.
Becky is taller than Dan. Viv is 3 cm shorter than Jake.

If the statements are true, only one of the sentences below **must** be true. Which one?

A Becky is 132 cm tall.

B Becky is shorter than Jake.

C Viv is taller than Dan.

D Maria is 120 cm tall.

E Jake is the tallest.

 / 1

5. Rita, Simon, Rose, Joe and Ernie took part in a javelin-throwing competition.
The shortest throw was 6 m. Simon threw the javelin further than Joe.
Ernie's was not the shortest throw. Rita threw the javelin the furthest.
Joe threw it twice as far as the shortest throw.

If the statements are true, only one of the sentences below **cannot** be true. Which one?

A Rose's throw was the shortest.

B Ernie threw the javelin further than Joe.

C Simon threw the javelin further than 12 m.

D Joe's was the third furthest throw.

E Ernie threw the javelin the same distance as Rose.

 / 1

6. Rob, Ian, Orla, Mo and Violet are comparing the outside temperature where they live.
The coldest temperature is 4.2° C. It is 0.8° C warmer where Rob lives than where Ian
lives. The warmest temperature is 2.6° C warmer than the second warmest temperature.
It is 5° C where Rob lives. The temperature where Orla lives is colder than where Mo
lives. It is 6.3° C where Mo lives.

If the statements are true, only one of the sentences below **cannot** be true. Which one?

A Violet lives in the warmest place.

B It is 4.8° C where Orla lives.

C Rob lives in the second warmest place.

D The warmest temperature is 8.9° C.

E Ian lives in the coldest place.

 / 1

Section Eight — Comprehension

Understanding the Language in the Text

Read the passage below, then answer the questions that follow.
Underline the correct option for each question.

"What was that?"

Grace nudged her brother Sam in the inky darkness, who sighed and rolled away. It was their first family camping trip and, after a lot of excitement, they'd both finally fallen asleep. Now, Grace had been rudely awoken by a strange rustling noise coming from outside. She

5   switched on her torch which illuminated the inside of the tent like a floodlight.

"I'm going to investigate," Grace whispered to Sam, who replied with a yawn.

Grace slipped on her boots, coat and hat: an explorer ready to venture into the unknown. She stepped out, and her sweeping torch beam came to rest on two eyes blinking in the darkness. The eyes belonged to a small sheep which was happily munching on grass.

10   "Well, you're certainly a very scary surprise!" said Grace, laughing softly to herself.

Hint: Read the question and each option carefully before you answer.

1. The author says that Sam "sighed" (line 2). What impression does this give you of Sam?

   A He is surprised.   **B** He is very worried.   **C** He is unconcerned.

2. The torch's beam is compared to a "floodlight" (line 5). What does this tell you?

   A The light is bright.   **B** The light is flashing.   **C** The light is yellow.

3. Why does Grace say that the sheep is "very scary" (line 10)?

   A She wants to scare Sam.   **B** She's being ironic.   **C** She's afraid of it.

4. Grace is described as an "explorer" (line 7). This suggests that she is:

   A brave.   **B** foolish.   **C** nervous.

5. The darkness is described as "inky" (line 2). This suggests that:

   A there are many shadows.   **B** it is very dark.   **C** it is barely dark.

6. At first, the author describes the sheep as "two eyes blinking in the darkness" (line 9).
   What effect does this have on the reader?

   A It creates a vivid setting.   **B** It creates humour.   **C** It creates tension.

/ 6

Understanding the Language in the Text

> Read the passage below, then answer the questions that follow.
> Underline the correct option for each question.

The distinctive red phone box has been a feature of the British high street for decades; the first of these phone boxes were installed in London in 1926. This initial structure, which weighed around a tonne and was designed by architect Sir Giles Scott, was striking but too large and costly to roll out across the country. In 1935, a new cast-iron design was

5   commissioned – weighing a quarter of a tonne less – and its use quickly spread across the UK, with more than 20 000 in existence by the turn of the decade.

In recent times, many phone boxes have fallen into disrepair — understandable given that most people now carry their own phone. However, some lucky boxes have been given a new lease of life by

10 innovative communities who have adopted them and turned them into libraries, local information points and even coffee shops.

1. What does the word "distinctive" (line 1) tell you about British phone boxes?

    A They are easily recognisable.   **B** They are popular.   **C** They are expensive.

2. Why was the cast-iron phone box more popular than the original design?

    A It was designed by Giles Scott.   **B** It was lighter.   **C** It was red.

3. How many phone boxes were there in the UK by 1940?

    A nearly 20 000   **B** exactly 20 000   **C** over 20 000

4. Why do you think the author says that it is "understandable" (line 8) that many phone boxes have fallen into disrepair?

    A Mobile phones are common.   **B** Phone boxes are tiny.   **C** People hate phones.

5. The author says that some phone boxes have been given "a new lease of life" (line 9). This means that they are:

    A being moved to new places.   **B** being used differently. **C** being knocked down.

6. The word "innovative" (line 10) tells you that the communities adopting phone boxes are:

    A stuck in the past.   **B** creative.   **C** working hard.

/ 6

Section Eight — Comprehension

Mixed Comprehension Questions

Read the passage below, then answer the questions that follow.

An abridged extract from 'The School by the Sea'

Please do not think because Miss Birks's pupils, on the first night of a new term, ran helter-skelter up and down the passages, and insisted on compulsory dancing or solo singing, that this was their normal course of procedure. It was but their one evening of liberty before they settled down to ordinary school routine, and for the rest of the

5   eighty-eight days before Easter their behaviour would be quite exemplary.

They were a very happy little community at the Dower House. They admired and respected their headmistress, and her well-framed rules were rarely transgressed. Certainly the girls would have been hard to please if they had not been satisfied with Miss Birks, for allied to her undoubted brain power she had those far rarer gifts of perfect tact and absolute

10   sympathy. She thoroughly understood that oft-time riddle, the mind of a schoolgirl, and, while still keeping her authority and maintaining the dignity of her position, could win her pupils' entire confidence almost as if she had been one of themselves.

"Miss Birks never seems to have quite grown up! She enjoys things just the same as we do," was the general verdict of the school.

15   Perhaps a strain of Irish in her genealogy had given the Principal the pleasant twinkle in her eye, the racy humour of speech, and the sunny optimistic view of life so dearly valued by all who knew her. Anyhow, whatever ancestry might claim to be the source of her cheery attributes, she had a very winning personality, and ruled her small kingdom with a hand so light that few realised its firmness. And a kingdom it was, in the girls' opinion — a veritable

20   "kingdom by the sea". No place in all the length and breadth of the British Isles, so they considered, could in any way compare with it. Together with the old castle, the Dower House stood on the neck of a long narrow peninsula that stretched for about two miles seaward. All the land on this little domain was the private property of Mrs. Trevellyan, who had granted full and entire leave for the pupils to wander where they wished. The result

25   of this generous concession was to give the girls a much larger amount of freedom than would have been possible in any other situation. The isolated position of the peninsula, only accessible through the Castle gateway, made it as safe and secluded a spot as a convent garden, and afforded a range of scenery that might well be a source of congratulation to those who enjoyed it.

by Angela Brazil

Mixed Comprehension Questions

> Answer these questions about the text.
> Circle the letter of the correct option for each question.

1. According to the passage, how did the girls run about on the first night of term?

   A In a calm, orderly manner

   B While shouting at the top of their voices

   C Quickly and from side to side

   D Slowly at first, then picking up speed

2. Why do you think the author compares a schoolgirl's mind to a "riddle" (line 10)?

   A Schoolgirls are very intelligent.

   B Schoolgirls have a good sense of humour.

   C It can be difficult to know what schoolgirls are thinking.

   D Schoolgirls are always planning something.

3. Which of the following is not given as a reason why the girls like Miss Birks?

   A She has certain things in common with them.

   B She lets the girls explore the school grounds.

   C She understands the girls well.

   D She is a positive person.

4. What do the girls think about the location of the Dower House?

   A They wish it were nearer to the castle.

   B They don't like how isolated it is.

   C They can't imagine a better place in Britain.

   D They think the scenery all looks the same.

5. Which statement best describes Miss Birks?

   A She is very stern and encourages a strict school routine.

   B She is very relaxed and lets the girls have a lot of freedom.

   C She sets lots of rules, but the girls don't follow them.

   D She is in charge but doesn't show off her authority.

/ 5

Turn over for the next question

Mixed Comprehension Questions

Answer these questions about the text on page 58.
Circle the letter of the correct option for each question.

6. The author tells the reader not to think that the girls' behaviour on the first night of term was "normal" (line 3). The author says this because:

    A they don't want the reader to get the wrong impression of the girls' behaviour.

    B they want to pretend that the girls are better behaved than they are.

    C they think Miss Birks should punish the girls for their behaviour.

    D they want to show that the girls at the Dower House are not like other girls.

7. Why do you think the author compares the peninsula to a "convent garden" (line 27-28)?

    A The girls are given a good religious education.

    B The girls are protected from danger.

    C The girls have to look after the plants and flowers.

    D The girls are able to speak privately to their friends.

8. What does the word "attributes" (line 18) mean?

    A Characteristics

    B Opinions

    C Expressions

    D Habits

9. What does the word "liberty" (line 4) mean?

    A Entertainment

    B Freedom

    C Chaos

    D Happiness

10. What does the word "transgressed" (line 7) mean?

    A Criticised

    B Changed

    C Disobeyed

    D Enforced

/ 5

Assessment Test 1

The rest of the book contains eight assessment tests, which get progressively harder.
Allow 40 minutes to do each test and work as quickly and as carefully as you can.

If you want to attempt each test more than once, you will need to print
multiple-choice answer sheets for these questions from our website
— go to cgpbooks.co.uk/11plus/answer-sheets or scan the QR code on the right.
If you'd prefer to answer the questions on the page, just follow the instructions in the question.

Answer Sheets

> Read this text carefully and answer the questions that follow.

An extract from 'The Magic Soap Bubble'

Ned and the Gnome continued their journey down the valley, following the crystal stream, in whose waters he had just a short time before seen his distorted figure, until they came to a beautiful waterfall, down whose silvery sheen slid numerous water sprites and water fairies.

"Over yonder," exclaimed the Gnome, "lives the Fairy of the Lake. She brews a magic liquid
5   from checkerberries, which, I am told, if you but drink a thimbleful, will enable you to regain your natural shape. There she goes now, over the bridge, on some such errand I dare say."

Ned watched the fairy stepping across the silver network which hung above a miniature Niagara* that he could easily have spanned with a single step. Catching up a handful of berries he followed her, not heeding the Gnome's remark "that she would probably prefer to pick them herself," and,
10 almost treading on some of the fairies who were blowing about in the long grass like the flowers they represented, threw the berries in a heap at the door of her castle.

It was, indeed, a most beautiful little palace. Made of brilliant crystals, it sparkled in the sun like a rainbow. Inside, it was even more exquisite, for all her little subjects, the flower fairies and the woodland fays*, had adorned it with many lovely things.

15 Ned stooped over and peeped in at the doorway. There was a bright light inside which came from a little star suspended from the ceiling, the crystal walls on all sides reflecting the light with great brilliancy. Here and there were draped beautiful laces, no doubt spun by the spiders kept by the fairies for that purpose.

"Come," said the Gnome somewhat impatiently, as Ned's curiosity still held him at the little
20 castle's doorway. "Come away, or else the Queen will not return. How is she to enter if you block up her entrance?"

*Niagara — *Niagara Falls, a famous waterfall*   *fays — *fairies*   **by David Cory**

> Answer these questions about the text that you've just read.
> Circle the letter of the correct answer.

1. Which word best describes the Gnome?

   A Helpful
   B Arrogant
   C Rude
   D Foolish

/ 1

Carry on to the next question → →

2. What is the Fairy of the Lake doing when Ned and the Gnome first see her?

    A Collecting checkerberries
    B Making a potion
    C Flying through the grass
    D Crossing over a waterfall

3. Why does Ned want a potion from the Fairy of the Lake?

    A He wants to gain magical powers.
    B He wants to become stronger.
    C He wants to return to his original form.
    D He wants to become taller.

4. According to the text, what do some of the fairies resemble?

    A Trees
    B Streams
    C Flowers
    D Rainbows

5. Which of the following statements is true?

    A Ned had seen a reflection of himself in a lake.
    B The Gnome has seen the Fairy of the Lake brew the potion.
    C The fairy bridge is made of crystal.
    D The Gnome isn't certain where the Fairy of the Lake is going.

6. How does Ned react when he sees the Fairy of the Lake?

    A He is afraid of her powers.
    B He is excited to tell people that he saw her.
    C He is impatient to speak to her.
    D He is surprised that she was so easy to find.

7. "Ned stooped over and peeped in at the doorway." (line 15)
   This sentence suggests that:

    A Ned has bad eyesight and can't see the palace clearly.
    B The fairies have hidden their palace well.
    C Ned is much bigger than the palace door.
    D Ned is worried that the fairies will see him looking.

8. The Gnome says "if you but drink a thimbleful" (line 5).
   What does this mean?

    A If you don't drink enough
    B If you drink only a small amount
    C If you drink too much
    D If you won't drink from a thimble

/ 7

9. What is meant by the word "exquisite" (line 13)?

   A Beautiful and delicate
   B Attractive and sturdy
   C Charming and sweet
   D Powerful and refined

10. What is meant by the word "distorted" (line 2)?

   A Misshapen
   B Partial
   C Unrecognisable
   D Injured

/ 2

Find the three-letter word that completes the word in capital letters, and finishes the sentence in a sensible way.

   Example: My family are going on **HOAY** to France.   (___LID___)

11. A **SUD** flash of lightning lit up the sky.   (_____)

12. Harpinder liked **WALG** her dog after school.   (_____)

13. The **WEAR** forecast for the weekend was awful.   (_____)

14. I had a **BL** with eggs and bacon for breakfast.   (_____)

15. Cook the spaghetti in a pan of **BING** water.   (_____)

16. Ewan always **FORS** his boots for football practice.   (_____)

17. These balloons will **EXD** when we blow them up.   (_____)

18. They **SLED** at us angrily as we walked past.   (_____)

/ 8

Find a word that completes the third pair of words so that it follows the same pattern as the first two pairs.

   Example: earn ear   bank ban   seat (___sea___)

19. glad lag   thin hit   team   (_____)

20. good dog   mile elm   plan   (_____)

21. court tour   learn near   baker (_____)

22. daily laid   grace crag   pride (_____)

23. scale lace   smite time   grade (_____)

24. appeal leap   medium mime   report (_____)

/ 6

Carry on to the next question → →

Find the pair of letters that continues each sequence in the best way. Use the alphabet to help you.

A B C D E F G H I J K L M N O P Q R S T U V W X Y Z

Example: AB   BC   CD   DE   EF   (__FG__)

25. FR   HO   JL   LI   NF   (_____)

26. JC   MH   PM   SR   VW   (_____)

27. PB   NX   LT   JP   HL   (_____)

28. MS   NU   OT   PV   QU   (_____)

29. WL   UO   VR   TU   UX   (_____)

30. DG   FE   ID   KB   NA   (_____)

31. AM   FN   CP   HS   EW   (_____)

32. YB   XA   VY   SX   OV   (_____)

/ 8

Mark the word outside the brackets that has a similar meaning to the words in both sets of brackets.

Example: (travel move)   (turn try)   effort advance attempt <u>go</u> drive

33. (ground earth)   (arrive dock)   soil anchor moor land property

34. (pierce puncture) (strike hit)   punch knock mark force blow

35. (perform act)   (participate compete) role play match stage pass

36. (build create)   (idea concept)   make notion establish view construct

37. (bore penetrate) (practice exercise) repetition tunnel drill break train

38. (parts sections) (lodgings rooms)   quarters posts shares regions houses

39. (quite rather)   (justly impartially) truly fairly honestly relatively really

/ 7

Find the missing number to complete each sum.

Example: $5 + 7 = 6 \times (\underline{\quad 2 \quad})$

40. $19 + 9 = (\underline{\qquad}) \times 7$

41. $12 + 3 = 5 \times (\underline{\qquad})$

42. $16 - 8 = (\underline{\qquad}) \div 3$

43. $34 \div 2 = 9 + (\underline{\qquad})$

/ 4

Each question uses a different code. Use the alphabet to help you work out the answer to each question.

A B C D E F G H I J K L M N O P Q R S T U V W X Y Z

Example: If the code for **ZIP** is **YHO**, what is the code for **RUN**? (_QTM_)

44. If the code for **DRAW** is **FTCY**, what is **HWGN** the code for? (_____)

45. If the code for **SHOT** is **RGNS**, what is **KHED** the code for? (_____)

46. If the code for **MUST** is **PXVW**, what is the code for **ZONE**? (_____)

47. If the code for **KING** is **JJMH**, what is the code for **READ**? (_____)

48. If the code for **TAPE** is **GZKV**, what is **TIRM** the code for? (_____)

49. If the code for **CITY** is **DKWC**, what is the code for **PAGE**? (_____)

50. If the code for **NOTE** is **MLGV**, what is **QFNK** the code for? (_____)

51. If the code for **BOND** is **DNPC**, what is **YZMD** the code for? (_____)   / 8

Three of the words in each list are linked. Mark the two words that are not related to these three.

Example: loud   noisy   <u>quiet</u>   rowdy   <u>peaceful</u>

52. horse   chicken   goose   dog   donkey

53. aubergine   broccoli   asparagus   pumpkin   celery

54. armadillo   fairy   platypus   troll   ogre

55. paint   artwork   brush   portrait   easel

56. country   song   music   jazz   pop

57. drawbridge   moat   castle   fortress   palace

58. citizen   owner   inhabitant   resident   voter

59. tedious   monotonous   diligent   dull   compulsive

60. calculation   difficulty   sum   protractor   problem

61. football   cycling   hockey   rugby   swimming

62. infectious   sombre   ghostly   morbid   gloomy

/ 11

> Find the word that means the same, or nearly the same, as the word on the left.
>
> **Example: stop**   begin   <u>halt</u>   start   go

63. **harsh**   brave   severe   wild   challenging

64. **famous**   mythical   successful   renowned   amiable

65. **entire**   sufficient   vast   whole   considerable

66. **feast**   nourishment   banquet   abstain   cuisine

67. **routine**   training   punctual   ordinary   irregular

68. **logical**   careful   valid   reasonable   objective

69. **dogged**   wild   earnest   persistent   tolerant

70. **immense**   colossal   dense   important   negligible

71. **appear**   immerse   ensue   exhibit   emerge

72. **inclination** preconception   tendency   question   aversion   / 10

> Read the information carefully, then use it to answer the question that follows.

73. Maisie, Orla, Seth, Adjoa and Bartek all buy souvenirs at a gift shop.

    Adjoa and Seth each buy a magnet. Everyone except Seth buys a key ring.
    Orla is the only one who does not buy a postcard. Bartek, Maisie and Seth
    each buy a pen. Maisie is the only one who buys a bookmark.

    Who buys the **most** items?   (_____)

74. Hafsa, Luke, Elliot, Kayla and Dafydd are discussing sports day events.

    Dafydd, Elliot and Kayla are each taking part in the obstacle course. Kayla, Luke
    and Hafsa are all taking part in the sack race. Everyone except for Luke is in the
    three-legged race. Kayla is the only child who isn't running in the relay.

    Who takes part in the **fewest** events?   (_____)   / 2

Total   / 74

End of Test

Assessment Test 2

Allow 40 minutes to do this test and work as quickly and as carefully as you can.

You can print **multiple-choice answer sheets** for these questions from our website — go to cgpbooks.co.uk/11plus/answer-sheets or scan the QR code on the right. If you'd prefer to answer the questions on the page, just follow the instructions in the question.

Answer Sheets

Read this text carefully and answer the questions that follow.

An extract from 'Nightfall in New York'

It was midnight in London. Lights were being extinguished; the theatres and restaurants were closing their doors. Street lamps glowed and on Piccadilly Circus, illuminated advertisements glittered. The windows of Sinclair's, London's most elegant department store, shimmered gold in the dark.

In Covent Garden, people slept huddled on the doorstep of an old church, under the yellowing
5 sheets of yesterday's newspaper. In Soho, a lone policeman strode down a narrow, cobbled passage. At the Inns of Court, all was silent — but on Fleet Street, the printing presses clattered through the night, churning out the papers that tomorrow the newsboys would be hawking on every corner.

In Westminster, Big Ben chimed midnight, slowly and solemnly. The policeman on duty outside 10 Downing Street heard it, and was glad. It was the end of his shift and he'd soon be home, toasting
10 his toes before a warm fire.

Behind him, the Prime Minister's residence was dark, but for the first-floor window of the study, which still glowed with yellow lamp light. Arthur Lockwood was working late.

The Prime Minister had not noticed Big Ben chiming. He was engrossed in his work, making his way through the contents of a red dispatch box. Methodically he set aside one document to
15 read later, before scrawling his initials upon another. The room was quiet but for the crackling of the fire, and the regular tick of the grandfather clock, marking time just as it had for every British Prime Minister since Gladstone. From an adjoining room came the tapping of the typewriter, and an occasional stifled yawn from the Prime Minister's private secretary who was hoping that Lockwood would soon retire for the night.

20 Just then, something made the Prime Minister pause. As he reached into the box to take out the next document, he saw something unexpected — a small envelope. It was still sealed, which was odd in itself. The other letters in the box had already been opened and reviewed by his staff. But this envelope was unopened, as if it had been slipped secretly amongst the rest by an unseen hand.

by Katherine Woodfine

Answer these questions about the text that you've just read.
Circle the letter of the correct answer.

1. Who is Arthur Lockwood?

   A A policeman
   B The Prime Minister
   C The Prime Minister's secretary
   D A typist

/ 1

Carry on to the next question → →

2. Which of the following statements is true?

    A Piccadilly Circus is in total darkness.
    B Lights in theatres and restaurants are being turned on.
    C The lights in the shops are still on.
    D The streets lights are on.

3. Which of the following is not mentioned in the passage?

    A Some famous London landmarks
    B The location of the printing presses
    C The name of the street where the Prime Minister lives
    D What the weather is like

4. Which word best describes the private secretary?

    A Furious
    B Weary
    C Uneasy
    D Inquisitive

5. What is unusual about the envelope that the Prime Minister finds?

    A It has not been opened.
    B It is small.
    C It has no writing on it.
    D It is the only envelope in the box.

6. How long has the grandfather clock been in the Prime Minister's study?

    A Since the Prime Minister came to power
    B Since Gladstone was in power
    C Since before Gladstone was in power
    D Since the Prime Minister's study was built

7. Which of the following statements is false?

    A The Prime Minister's study is upstairs.
    B There is a fire in the Prime Minister's study.
    C The Prime Minister and private secretary are in the same room.
    D The Prime Minister's study is lit up by lamps.

8. The printing presses are described as "churning out" newspapers (line 7). What does this mean?

    A They are producing lots of newspapers very quickly.
    B It requires lots of effort for them to produce newspapers.
    C They are producing poor-quality newspapers.
    D The process of producing newspapers creates a loud noise.

/ 7

9. What is meant by the phrase "engrossed in" (line 13)?

   A Surrounded by
   B Frustrated by
   C Committed to
   D Absorbed in

10. What is meant by the word "Methodically" (line 14)?

   A Ruthlessly
   B Systematically
   C Thoughtlessly
   D Slowly

/ 2

Mark the word outside the brackets that has a similar meaning to the words in both sets of brackets.

   Example: (travel move)   (turn try)   effort advance attempt <u>go</u>

11. (discard drop)   (pigsty hovel)   hole leave dump trash

12. (casket locker)   (bosom breast)   case box chest bust

13. (estate premises)   (reason justification)   basis grounds domain realm

14. (ambition desire)   (ride trip)   effort aim commute drive

15. (combined shared)   (hinge connection)   seam mutual joint union

16. (plot area)   (fix mend)   patch spot sort repair

17. (figure miniature)   (perfect ideal)   standard replica model example

18. (fixed secure)   (founded began)   initiated established stable set

19. (minor unknown)   (hide conceal)   dark obscure cover disguise

20. (sketch draft)   (aim intention)   design pattern hope object

/ 10

Mark two words, one from each set of brackets, that have the most similar meaning.

   Example: (<u>run</u> swim dance)   (walk jump <u>sprint</u>)

21. (roof pillar building)   (wall assemble column)

22. (mob bustle brawl)   (crowded violent gang)

23. (saw panel axe)   (board fire tree)

24. (book title chapter)   (series section page)

25. (pack expand fill)   (grow pull increase)

/ 5

Carry on to the next question → →

Find the pair of letters that continues each sequence in the best way. Use the alphabet to help you.

A B C D E F G H I J K L M N O P Q R S T U V W X Y Z

Example: AB   BC   CD   DE   EF   (__FG__)

26. EI   GL   IO   KR   MU   (_____)

27. KH   IE   GB   EY   CV   (_____)

28. DO   EM   GK   JI   NG   (_____)

29. AK   CI   BG   DE   CC   (_____)

30. VH   XF   YE   AC   BB   (_____)

31. SV   SV   TU   VS   YP   (_____)

/ 6

Mark a word from the first set, followed by a word from the second set, that go together to form a new word.

Example: (care <u>any</u> fly)   (wash wear <u>thing</u>)   (the new word is 'anything')

32. (tread   light   fire)   (brow   mill   paper)

33. (ship   sea   sail)   (nick   oar   yard)

34. (above   down   through)   (side   top   bottom)

35. (brake   time   new)   (under   fast   born)

36. (chain   eye   see)   (link   sore   side)

37. (snip   cut   trim)   (tap   hand   pet)

/ 6

In each sentence below a four-letter word is hidden at the end of one word and the start of the next. **Either** mark the part of the sentence that contains the hidden word on the answer sheet, **or** write the hidden word on the line.

Example: The large glo<u>be st</u>opped spinning quickly.   (__best__)

38. Sofia always eats her packed lunch.   (_____)

39. The unusual guest's briefcase was hefty.   (_____)

40. Everyone volunteered at the first opportunity.   (_____)

41. The thunderstorm was over before lunchtime.   (_____)

42. Can anyone mend my broken umbrella?   (_____)

43. Dad helped get the children ready.   (_____)

/ 6

Fill in the missing letters to complete the words in the following passage.

44. The whistle blew, and Charlie ☐ i v ☐ d into the water.

45. As he broke the s u ☐ ☐ ☐ c e of the pool, the intense cold almost made him gasp,

46. but he c ☐ ☐ m p ☐ d his mouth shut and concentrated on kicking his legs.

47. He could still hear the buzz of c ☐ ☐ ☐ r i n g spectators from the gallery,

48. but the sounds were now m ☐ f f ☐ ☐ d, as if they were happening far away.

49. ☐ u ☐ d e ☐ ☐ y , his head shot up through the water,

50. and the frantic sounds of s p ☐ ☐ ☐ h i n g and shouting flooded his ears.

51. Instinctively, he twisted his head and took a deep ☐ r e ☐ t ☐ .

52. His arms got to work, propelling him f ☐ ☐ w ☐ r d through the clear water.

53. Just as he was settling into a ☐ h y t ☐ ☐ , the far end of the pool snapped into focus.

54. Without needing to think, he tumbled and t ☐ ☐ ☐ e d , kicking off the wall.

55. It was only at this point that his t h ☐ ☐ ☐ ☐ t s turned to the other swimmers.

56. Every time he twisted his head to breathe, he caught g ☐ i ☐ p ☐ ☐ s of them

57. moving in and out of his v i ☐ ☐ o n as they raced alongside him.

58. It was c ☐ r t ☐ ☐ n ☐ ☐ going to be a close finish.

/ 15

The words in the second set follow the same pattern as the words in the first set. Find the missing word to complete the second set.

Example: dose (let) flat   area (__oat__) host

59. tape (pie) fin   rift (_____) ham

60. sort (top) pox   else (_____) fur

61. fear (rag) grab   stub (_____) nice

62. glue (gel) lag   diva (_____) top

63. wash (was) sew   cell (_____) dew

64. rasp (skip) sink   fort (_____) once

/ 6

Carry on to the next question → →

Assessment Test 2

Find the word that means the opposite, or nearly the opposite, of the word on the left.

Example: **large**   big   enormous   giant   <u>small</u>

65. **awful**   unusual   pleasant   horrid   lively

66. **wild**   furious   ordinary   caring   calm

67. **begin**   raise   conclude   continue   prevent

68. **unfit**   stable   suitable   broken   ordinary

69. **wise**   unskilled   frantic   evil   foolish

70. **inject**   injure   extract   prevent   cure

71. **tempt**   repulse   benefit   concern   terrify

72. **distort**   truth   redeem   twist   straighten   / 8

Read the information carefully, then use it to answer the question that follows.

73. Tim, Beth, Charlotte, Sammy and Sunita all went running. Beth ran 10 km.
    Tim ran the same distance as Charlotte. Sunita started running after Beth.
    Sammy ran 5 km further than anyone else. Charlotte ran further than Beth.

    If these statements are true, only one of the sentences below **must** be true. Which one?

    A Sammy ran 25 km.
    B Sunita ran further than Tim.
    C Charlotte is the fastest runner.
    D Tim ran further than 10 km.
    E Beth ran faster than Sunita.

74. Isla, Parker, Amanda, Yusuf and Sven are discussing how many cousins they have.
    Everyone has at least one cousin. Parker and Yusuf have four cousins each. Sven has twice
    as many cousins as Amanda. Isla has the fewest number of cousins.

    If these statements are true, only one of the sentences below **cannot** be true. Which one?

    A Isla only has one cousin.
    B All of Parker's cousins are girls.
    C Yusuf has more cousins than Sven.
    D Sven has an even number of cousins.
    E Amanda has three cousins.   / 2

Total   / 74

End of Test

Assessment Test 3

Allow 40 minutes to do this test and work as quickly and as carefully as you can.

You can print **multiple-choice answer sheets** for these questions from our website — go to cgpbooks.co.uk/11plus/answer-sheets or scan the QR code on the right. If you'd prefer to answer the questions on the page, just follow the instructions in the question.

Answer Sheets

> Read this text carefully and answer the questions that follow.

Plastic Beach

Seeking a momentary escape from the disheartening truth in front of me, I closed my eyes and tried to envisage what Kamilo Beach looked like before humans populated our fragile planet. My mind was filled with a captivating vision of sparkling waves depositing seashells onto a clear stretch of sand. Reluctantly, I opened my eyes and was confronted by a seemingly infinite expanse of plastic debris,
5 which drowned the once-golden shore and stretched as far as I could see.

Located on the southern tip of Hawaii, Kamilo Beach appears to be a magnet for unrecycled plastic drifting aimlessly in the surrounding Pacific Ocean. This has caused it to become known as one of the most plastic-polluted locations in the world, hence the unsettling name 'Plastic Beach'.

Covering over 70% of the Earth's surface, the world's oceans are home to many marine
10 ecosystems. One of the greatest threats facing marine life is the millions of tonnes of plastic entering the oceans every year. This vast amount of plastic, which circulates around the globe on ocean currents, can prove fatal to marine animals, as many become entangled in larger plastic pieces that limit their movement and cause injuries. Over time, most plastic breaks down into tiny fragments called microplastics, which pose an additional threat to marine life, as they can be toxic when ingested.

15 So what can you do to help keep plastic out of our oceans? While widespread change relies heavily on shifts in government policy, cutting down on the amount of single-use plastics in your day-to-day life is a great way to individually make a difference. For example, you could invest in a reusable water bottle rather than buying bottled water. If you can't avoid single-use plastics, make sure you recycle them properly afterwards. Most ocean plastic, whether incorrectly sent to landfill or
20 left outside as litter, enters the ocean by being blown into rivers and carried out to sea.

I am cautiously optimistic that one day Kamilo Beach will return to its former pristine glory, as will all the other beaches currently swamped by plastic debris. Now the question remains — will you be part of the endeavour to save our seas from plastic pollution?

> Answer these questions about the text that you've just read.
> Circle the letter of the correct answer.

1. What is the "disheartening truth" mentioned in line 1?

   A That Kamilo Beach will soon disappear
   B That Kamilo Beach is covered in plastic
   C That Kamilo Beach has been ruined by visitors
   D That Kamilo Beach will never look beautiful again

/ 1

Carry on to the next question → →

74

2. According to the passage, which of the following statements is false?

   A Water covers over half of the Earth's surface.
   B Hawaii is located in the Pacific Ocean.
   C Only governments are responsible for reducing plastic pollution.
   D Ocean currents transport plastic around the world.

3. Which adjective best describes the writer's tone in lines 21-23 of the passage?

   A Hopeful
   B Confident
   C Doubtful
   D Cynical

4. According to the passage, which of the following statements must be true?

   A The ocean contains just under one million tonnes of plastic.
   B Sea creatures are sometimes killed by plastic.
   C Microplastics are more harmful than larger plastics.
   D Litter left inland can't reach the coast.

5. Which of the following is not mentioned in the passage?

   A How you can cut down on single-use plastics
   B How you should dispose of single-use plastics
   C Where microplastics come from
   D How long it takes for microplastics to form

6. Which of the following best describes how the writer feels about the name "Plastic Beach"?

   A Disbelieving
   B Irritated
   C Troubled
   D Disgusted

7. Which of the following is not one of the writer's aims in writing the text?

   A To achieve a complete ban of all single-use plastics
   B To educate people about microplastics
   C To convince people to recycle more plastic
   D To raise awareness about the dangers of plastic

8. What is meant by the word "pristine" (line 21)?

   A Untouched
   B Barren
   C Beautiful
   D Peaceful

/ 7

Assessment Test 3

9. What is meant by the word "infinite" (line 4)?

   A Irreversible
   B Growing
   C Dense
   D Limitless

10. What is meant by the phrase "Kamilo Beach appears to be a magnet for unrecycled plastic" (lines 6-7)?

   A Plastic builds up on Kamilo Beach before being washed out to sea.
   B A large amount of plastic washes up on Kamilo Beach.
   C People tend to bring their plastic rubbish to Kamilo Beach.
   D Most of the world's plastic ends up on Kamilo Beach.

/ 2

Find the number that completes the final set of numbers in the same way as the first two sets.

Example: 1 (3) 5   12 (14) 16   8 (__10__) 12

11. 5 (19) 14   14 (22) 8   12 (_____) 9

12. 7 (28) 4   9 (18) 2   6 (_____) 8

13. 4 (17) 3   6 (23) 3   7 (_____) 2

14. 6 (5) 16   4 (7) 18   10 (_____) 28

15. 9 (20) 2   7 (24) 3   6 (_____) 6

16. 42 (12) 7   40 (16) 5   30 (_____) 6

/ 6

Each letter stands for a number. Work out the answer to each sum as a letter.

Example: A = 2   B = 3   C = 4   D = 6   E = 8   E ÷ A = (__C__)

17. A = 3   B = 4   C = 8   D = 13   E = 14   B + D − E = (_____)

18. A = 2   B = 3   C = 5   D = 11   E = 15   B × A + C = (_____)

19. A = 3   B = 4   C = 6   D = 12   E = 24   E ÷ A − B = (_____)

20. A = 2   B = 4   C = 7   D = 9   E = 14   C × B ÷ A = (_____)

21. A = 6   B = 8   C = 10   D = 16   E = 22   E + B − D − A = (_____)

22. A = 2   B = 3   C = 6   D = 18   E = 21   E ÷ B + A − C = (_____)

/ 6

Carry on to the next question → →

Assessment Test 3

Find the letter that will finish the first word and start the second word of each pair. The same letter must be used for both pairs. **Either** mark the letter on the answer sheet, **or** write it on the line.

Example: hol (?) ry   lan (?) oom   __d__

23. fla (?) old   fee (?) ear   (_____)

24. rai (?) and   coi (?) ife   (_____)

25. swa (?) ale   su (?) ess   (_____)

26. ble (?) ilt   tha (?) ood   (_____)

27. tan (?) een   pea (?) ind   (_____)

28. fle (?) amp   mai (?) ove   (_____)

29. lea (?) ose   see (?) lot   (_____)   / 7

Three of the words in each list are linked. Mark the two words that are not related to these three.

Example: loud   noisy   <u>quiet</u>   rowdy   <u>peaceful</u>

30. postcard   pencil   letter   paper   note

31. authentic   reliable   dependable   real   genuine

32. grate   bitter   chop   bland   spicy

33. describe   envision   picture   illustrate   imagine   / 4

Mark two words, one from each set of brackets, that complete the sentence in the most sensible way.

Example: **Eye** is to (face blink <u>see</u>) as **mouth** is to (<u>taste</u> tongue lips).

34. **Chauffeur** is to (drive car profession) as **actor** is to (drama role perform).

35. **Seesaw** is to (seat balance playground) as **popcorn** is to (food cinema snack).

36. **Mammoth** is to (tusks big tall) as **puny** is to (minor narrow small).

37. **Centimetres** is to (metres ruler length) as **hours** is to (time schedule minutes).

38. **Hollow** is to (space solid hole) as **occupied** is to (empty lost needless).

39. **Alligator** is to (reptile scales swamp) as **gorilla** is to (monkey mammal strength).   / 6

Complete the word on the right so that it means the same, or nearly the same, as the word on the left.

Example: fix [r][e][p][a][i][r]

40. **agitated** [r][ ][s][t][ ][ ][ ][s]

41. **discourage** [d][ ][ ][e][r]

42. **aim** [a][ ][p][i][ ][ ]

43. **upset** [d][ ][s][m][ ][ ][e][d]

44. **threaten** [ ][ ][d][ ][n][ ][e][r]

45. **dependence** [ ][ ][l][i][ ][ ][c][e]

46. **generosity** [ ][h][a][r][ ][t][ ]

47. **guarantee** [e][ ][s][ ][r][ ]

48. **gushed** [s][u][ ][ ][ ][d]

49. **hugged** [ ][ ][b][ ][a][c][ ][d]

50. **unbroken** [ ][n][ ][a][c][ ]

51. **exclude** [b][ ][n][ ][ ][h]

/ 12

Remove one letter from the first word and add it to the second word to make two new words. Do not rearrange the other letters. **Either** mark the letter that moves on the answer sheet, **or** write two new words on the lines.

Example: event hop (__vent__) (__hope__)

52. title hem (_____) (_____)

53. drive pot (_____) (_____)

54. found son (_____) (_____)

55. flair rue (_____) (_____)

56. thank air (_____) (_____)

57. debut nit (_____) (_____)

/ 6

Carry on to the next question → →

Assessment Test 3

Find a word that completes the third pair of words so that it follows the same pattern as the first two pairs.

Example: earn ear   bank ban   seat (__sea__)

58. tired dire   waste east   wider   (_____)

59. female meal   backed cake   debate (_____)

60. battle late   source core   treaty (_____)

61. reward wear   silent lies   sample (_____)

62. attempt team   somehow mesh   explain (_____)

63. passage gasp   explore role   receipt (_____)

64. chance each   reader rare   leaves (_____)

/ 7

Find the missing number to complete each sum.

Example: $5 + 7 = 6 \times (\underline{\quad 2 \quad})$

65. $41 + 7 = (\underline{\quad\quad}) \times 6$

66. $3 \times 5 = 24 - (\underline{\quad\quad})$

67. $32 \div 4 = 2 \times (\underline{\quad\quad})$

68. $13 + 11 - 6 = 3 \times (\underline{\quad\quad})$

69. $9 \times 5 + 5 = 40 + (\underline{\quad\quad})$

70. $24 \div 2 - 3 = 4 + (\underline{\quad\quad})$

71. $33 \div 3 \times 2 = (\underline{\quad\quad}) - 8$

72. $7 \times 4 \div 2 + 5 = (\underline{\quad\quad}) - 4$

73. $43 - 21 + 7 - 13 = 4 \times (\underline{\quad\quad})$

74. $20 \div 5 \times 7 \div 2 = 25 - (\underline{\quad\quad})$

/ 10

Total   / 74

End of Test

Assessment Test 4

Allow 40 minutes to do this test and work as quickly and as carefully as you can.

You can print **multiple-choice answer sheets** for these questions from our website — go to cgpbooks.co.uk/11plus/answer-sheets or scan the QR code on the right. If you'd prefer to answer the questions on the page, just follow the instructions in the question.

Answer Sheets

Read this poem carefully and answer the questions that follow.

Adapted from 'Death of the Old Sea King'

'Twas a fearful night — the tempest raved
With loud and wrathful pride,
The storm king harnessed his lightning steeds*,
And rode on the raging tide.

5   The sea king lay on his bed of death,
Pale mourners around him bent;
They knew the wild and fitful life
Of their chief was almost spent.

His ear was growing dull in death
10 When the angry storm he heard,
The sluggish blood in the old man's veins
With sudden vigour stirred.

"I can hear them call," cried the dying man,
His eyes grew full of light;
15 "Now bring me here my warrior robes,
My sword and armour bright.

*steeds — horses

"Bear me unto my noblest ship,
Light up a funeral pyre;
I'll walk to the palace of the braves
20 Through a path of flame and fire."

Oh! wild and bright was the stormy light
That flashed from the old man's eye,
As they bore him from the couch of death
To his battle-ship to die,

25 And lit with many a mournful torch
The sea king's dying bed,
And like a banner fair and bright
The flames around him spread.

Through a path of fearful splendour,
30 While strong men held their breath,
The brave old man went boldly forth
And calmly talked with death.

by Frances Harper

Answer these questions about the text that you've just read.
Circle the letter of the correct answer.

1.   What is being described in verse 1?

   A   A storm
   B   A journey
   C   An argument
   D   A battle

/ 1

2. Which of the following best describes the sea king's life?

   A Short and fulfilling
   B Conventional and stable
   C Long and peaceful
   D Dramatic and unsettled

3. What causes the sea king to rouse himself from his bed in verses 3-4?

   A He hears his enemies approaching.
   B He hears the storm outside.
   C He sees his sword and armour.
   D He sees a sudden ray of light.

4. Where is the sea king when he dies?

   A On his bed
   B On his sofa
   C On his horse
   D On his ship

5. Which of the following statements is true?

   A The sea king only owns one ship.
   B The sea king is afraid of dying.
   C The sea king tries to avoid his death.
   D The sea king dresses as a soldier for his death.

6. What are we told about the sea king in verse 7?

   A He looks brighter because of the fire.
   B He is injured by the flames.
   C He carries a banner through the fire.
   D He is mourned by lots of people.

7. The narrator describes how the sea king's life "was almost spent" (line 8).
   What does this mean?

   A He lived an extravagant lifestyle.
   B He was close to death.
   C He had nearly achieved all his life ambitions.
   D He still had lots to do before he died.

8. The narrator describes how the sea king's "ear was growing dull" (line 9).
   What do you think this phrase means?

   A He was becoming boring.
   B His ear was turning pale.
   C He was losing his hearing.
   D He was getting tired.

/ 7

9. What is meant by the word "splendour" (line 29)?

   A Surprise
   B Magnificence
   C Squalor
   D Curiosity

10. What is meant by the word "wrathful" (line 2)?

   A Boastful
   B Just
   C Angry
   D Arrogant

/ 2

Circle the letters which correspond to the correct words to complete the passage below.

Born in China in 1768, Wang Zhenyi was an

11. **A** architect
    B influential
    C famous
    D irritated

scholar and

12. **A** astronomer
    B science
    C character
    D astronaut

.

At that time, women were

13. **A** expected
    B restricted
    C permitted
    D inspired

to stay at home, and

14. **A** little
    B few
    C less
    D many

women received a

formal

15. **A** idea
    B appetite
    C success
    D education

. Zhenyi was

16. **A** unusual
    B alone
    C fortunate
    D victorious

that she was born into an

17. **A** elated
    B utmost
    C affluent
    D kind

family who

18. **A** encouraged
    B suggested
    C signalled
    D threatened

her to study a variety of subjects. Her

19. **A** many
    B chief
    C new
    D rare

interests were

Astronomy and Mathematics, and she was especially

20. **A** apathetic
    B curious
    C absorbed
    D fascinated

by eclipses. She worked hard

to

21. **A** simplify
    B sell
    C read
    D inscribe

difficult mathematical texts so that others could

22. **A** compose
    B calculate
    C understand
    D pursue

them more easily.

23. **A** Besides
    B Even
    C Also
    D However

this, she was a

24. **A** average
    B direct
    C modern
    D talented

poet and published several volumes of her work.

/ 14

She was only 29 when she died, but her legacy endures today.

Carry on to the next question → →

Assessment Test 4

Fill in the missing letters to complete the words in the following passage.

25. With its summit at 8,611 metres [a b o v e] sea level, K2 is the world's second-tallest

26. mountain, its height [e x c e e d e d] only by Mount Everest. Due to its freezing

27. temperatures and [g i g a n t i c] size, K2 is infamous for being one of the most

28. [d a n g e r o u s] mountains to climb. Many stare up at its towering peak with

29. trepidation, thinking of the countless climbers who have [f a i l e d] to reach the summit.

30. Those brave enough to [a t t e m p t] the climb usually do so in July or August,

31. as the risk of snowstorms is [l o w e r]. However, even at this time of year, the

32. extreme cold can be [d e a d l y]. Climbers also face the risk of running low on

33. oxygen, as it is [h a r d e r] to breathe at higher altitudes. Therefore, it is recommended

34. that only experienced mountaineers take on the [c h a l l e n g e].   / 10

Find the word that means the opposite, or nearly the opposite, of the word on the left.

Example: large   big   enormous   giant   <u>small</u>

35. **peaceful**   inconsistent   irritating   hectic   disorganised

36. **emphasise**   question   understate   reduce   forget

37. **miserable**   relieved   energetic   elated   calm

38. **hide**   exhibit   abandon   decorate   discover

39. **convinced**   ignorant   sceptical   disinterested   ironic

40. **distracted**   excited   captivated   thoughtful   determined

41. **respect**   harm   abandon   provoke   disobey

42. **continue**   reject   prohibit   fail   cease

43. **discourage**   intrigue   revive   bolster   relieve

44. **effortless**   uncertain   gruelling   detailed   tolerable

/ 10

In each sentence below a four-letter word is hidden at the end of one word and the start of the next. **Either** mark the part of the sentence that contains the hidden word on the answer sheet, **or** write the hidden word on the line.

Example: The large glo<u>be st</u>opped spinning quickly. (_best_)

45. Katie's classmates always suggest clever ideas. (_____)

46. Can you look indoors for cutlery? (_____)

47. Our carriage arrived extremely late again. (_____)

48. Mara hurt her knee doing gymnastics. (_____)

49. We have ages until the holidays. (_____)

50. Ishir devoured the tremendous picnic eagerly. (_____)

/ 6

Find the number that completes the final set of numbers in the same way as the first two sets.

Example: 1 (3) 5   12 (14) 16   8 (_10_) 12

51. 6 (48) 8   3 (27) 9   7 (_____) 5

52. 7 (12) 17   13 (22) 31   11 (_____) 15

53. 6 (10) 9   4 (7) 8   3 (_____) 4

54. 20 (5) 10   13 (3) 7   17 (_____) 5

55. 7 (30) 3   11 (45) 4   6 (_____) 2

/ 5

Remove one letter from the first word and add it to the second word to make two new words. Do not rearrange the other letters. **Either** mark the letter that moves on the answer sheet, **or** write two new words on the lines.

Example: event   hop   (_vent_) (_hope_)

56. chomp   far   (_____) (_____)

57. flake   pie   (_____) (_____)

58. midst   boy   (_____) (_____)

59. bound   ant   (_____) (_____)

60. noise   bat   (_____) (_____)

/ 5

Carry on to the next question → →

Assessment Test 4

Find the number that continues each sequence in the best way.

Example: 3, 5, 7, 9, 11, (__13__)

61. **2, 5, 7, 12,** (_____)

62. **1, 13, 6, 20, 11, 27,** (_____)

63. **2, 2, 4, 12,** (_____)

64. **48, 2, 24, 6, 12, 18,** (_____)

65. **70, 45, 29, 20,** (_____)

/ 5

Mark two words, one from each set of brackets, that complete the sentence in the most sensible way.

Example: **Eye** is to (face blink <u>see</u>) as **mouth** is to (<u>taste</u> tongue lips).

66. **Knight** is to (soldier sword army) as **wizard** is to (wand prophecy enchant).

67. **Vile** is to (unwanted corrupt disgusting) as **prized** is to (valued guarded expensive).

68. **Torch** is to (bright battery see) as **compass** is to (spin navigate round).

69. **Water** is to (fluid hydrate transparent) as **air** is to (wind oxygen gas).

70. **Cube** is to (symmetrical volume solid) as **square** is to (area plane dimensions).

71. **Turbulent** is to (peaceful effortless distinct) as **affluent** is to (wealthy poor sparse).

/ 6

The number codes for three of these four words are listed in a random order. Work out the code to answer the questions.

TEAR   RATS   GATE   STAR

1346   2345   6431

72. Find the code for the word **TEAR**.   (_____)

73. Find the code for the word **RAGE**.   (_____)

74. Find the word that has the number code **2531**.   (_____)

/ 3

Total | / 74

End of Test

Assessment Test 5

Allow 40 minutes to do this test and work as quickly and as carefully as you can.

You can print **multiple-choice answer sheets** for these questions from our website — go to cgpbooks.co.uk/11plus/answer-sheets or scan the QR code on the right. If you'd prefer to answer the questions on the page, just follow the instructions in the question.

Answer Sheets

> Read this text carefully and answer the questions that follow.

An extract from 'Lost on Mars'

Da stared into the boiling soup of the red skies. 'See that?' He nodded to the far horizons, where a peppery darkness was building up like a swarm on its way. 'That's what's heading here.' He sighed, gazing at the swaying green of the cornstalks. I looked round and saw how little we had actually tackled. Only a tiny portion of the precious crop would be saved and I could feel the terrible
5 weight of Da's sadness. All that work of his would be ruined within minutes of the dust storm touching down.

And so we worked with renewed concentration and vigour. I was amazed at Toaster's speed. He tore into the cornrows, both hydraulic* arms lashing out with mechanical precision. Dry chaff* and waste flew in all directions as he worked.

10 It wasn't too much later when Da stopped us all. 'I was too generous in my estimation,' he said. 'I think we'd better go home now.'

It was barely three hours into the afternoon and a dry, nasty wind was rippling through the corn. It lashed at us like hot tongues saying bad things at our backs. Ma and Da and Al and Toaster worked busily packing up all the equipment, and covering up the panniers* of fresh-cut corn.

15 Staring into the storm as it lowered on down through the heaving clouds, I imagined a whole desertful of sand up there, flying about. About to slice right through us. Everything living would be torn to shreds. Wild grit was flying through the air and landing in our hair, stinging our exposed skin. Ma tucked Hannah into her arms.

'How long have we got?' she shouted at Da. 'Do we have time to get home?'

20 Da looked like he knew he'd cut it fine. He'd kept us out till the very last minute. He frowned and shook his head. 'Of course we've got time. If we go now, and we don't stop.'

by Paul Magrs

*hydraulic — *water-powered*
*chaff — the *outer layer of corn*
*panniers — *baskets*

> Answer these questions about the text that you've just read.
> Circle the letter of the correct answer.

1. Which word best describes how Da feels at the start of the text?

  A Furious
  B Confused
  C Suspicious
  D Dejected

/ 1

Carry on to the next question → →

2. Which of the following best describes how Toaster collects the corn?

    A Lazily and haphazardly
    B Clumsily and messily
    C Quickly and accurately
    D Recklessly and frantically

3. Which of the following is not mentioned in the text?

    A What time of day it is
    B How long the dust storm will last
    C How quickly the dust storm will destroy the corn
    D The colour of the sky

4. Which of the following statements is true?

    A The group packs up soon after Da points out the storm.
    B Da doesn't think they have enough time to get home.
    C Ma convinces Da to pack up and leave.
    D Toaster carries on working while the others pack up.

5. Why do you think Ma cradles Hannah close to her?

    A To stop her from running away
    B To shield her from the dust storm
    C To comfort her and stop her from crying
    D To keep her warm

6. Which of the following statements is false?

    A The storm approaches the group quickly.
    B The narrator doesn't help with all of the tasks.
    C The newly cut corn is stored safely.
    D Most of the corn has been harvested.

7. Which of the following best describes the narrator's feelings towards Da?

    A They feel compassionate because Da is losing his hard work.
    B They feel frustrated because Da is making them work.
    C They feel angry because Da has kept them in the field for so long.
    D They feel grateful because Da has rescued them from the storm.

8. What is meant by the word "exposed" (line 17)?

    A Grazed
    B Delicate
    C Ashen
    D Bare

/ 7

9. What is meant by the word "vigour" (line 7)?

   A Skill
   B Optimism
   C Energy
   D Nervousness

10. What do you think Da means when he says, "I was too generous in my estimation" (line 10)?

   A He originally thought the storm would miss the cornfield.
   B He misjudged how soon the storm would arrive.
   C He gave the others too much work to do.
   D He underestimated how much corn there was to harvest.

   / 2

Find the number that completes the final set of numbers in the same way as the first two sets.

Example: 1 (3) 5   12 (14) 16   8 (__10__) 12

---

11. 10 (4) 12   3 (13) 14   10 (____) 24

12. 2 (24) 13   6 (28) 5   7 (____) 4

13. 8 (12) 3   22 (44) 4   14 (____) 6

14. 7 (4) 56   6 (3) 36   7 (____) 28

15. 8 (5) 12   12 (8) 20   16 (____) 24

16. 13 (19) 25   9 (14) 19   26 (____) 32

   / 6

Read the information carefully, then use it to answer the question that follows.

17. Sienna, Izana, Matty, Bridget and Saoirse all go to the aquarium.

   Three of the children see a shark. Matty, Bridget and Izana all see a seahorse.
   Everyone except Izana sees an octopus. Matty and Izana see a stingray but not a turtle,
   whereas Sienna sees both. Bridget and Matty are disappointed to miss the shark.

   Who sees the **most** sea creatures?   (_____)

18. Ujala, Charmaine, Ray, Wyatt and Frank are discussing their weekend plans.

   On Saturday, Ujala, Frank and Ray are going skating together. Afterwards,
   Ray is meeting Charmaine for dinner, and then they are going to the cinema.
   Wyatt can't join them because he's going to a party, and Frank is going with him.
   On Sunday, Ujala and Frank plan to play video games together.

   Who has the **fewest** activities planned? (_____)

   / 2

Carry on to the next question → →

Fill in the missing letters to complete the words in the following passage.

19. Kamala trudged along the beach, her head **b**_ **w**_ _ against the fierce wind.

20. In the _ **i s t** _ _ **c** _ , the Ferris wheel towered above the other rides,

21. its empty seats swaying. She loved this time of year, when all the _ _ **s** _ **t** _ **r s**

22. had gone home and the only sounds were the **f** _ _ **l o** _ **n** shrieks of gulls and the

23. relentless pounding of waves _ _ **a i** _ **s t** the pier. In the summer, she often felt

24. like an impostor, a lonely, solemn figure amongst all the happy **f** _ _ _ _ **i e s**

25. busily **b** _ _ **l** _ **i n** _ sand castles and eating enormous ice creams.

26. But, for the **w** _ **n t** _ _ at least, the town was hers and hers alone.

/ 8

Each question uses a different code. Use the alphabet to help you work out the answer to each question.

A B C D E F G H I J K L M N O P Q R S T U V W X Y Z

Example: If the code for **ZIP** is **YHO**, what is the code for **RUN**? (**QTM**)

27. If the code for **PARK** is **NCPM**, what is **UQMF** the code for? (_____)

28. If the code for **VERSE** is **EVIHV**, what is **PMLXP** the code for? (_____)

29. If the code for **JUDGE** is **GWAIB**, what is the code for **DREAM**? (_____)

30. If the code for **TIGER** is **TJIHV**, what is the code for **FLAME**? (_____)

31. If the code for **ALARM** is **ZOZIN**, what is **MRTSG** the code for? (_____)

32. If the code for **GLEAM** is **FJBWH**, what is the code for **SHINE**? (_____)

33. If the code for **PLAN** is **QOFU**, what is **JGJH** the code for? (_____)

/ 7

Each letter stands for a number. Work out the answer to each sum as a letter.

Example: A = 2   B = 3   C = 4   D = 6   E = 8 $E \div A = ($ **C** $)$

34. A = 4   B = 7   C = 8   D = 14   E = 20 $B \times A - E = ($ _____ $)$

35. A = 2   B = 3   C = 12   D = 16   E = 24 $E \div B \times A = ($ _____ $)$

36. A = 4   B = 6   C = 8   D = 16   E = 18 $C \times A \div D + B = ($ _____ $)$

37. A = 3   B = 8   C = 10   D = 15   E = 20 $D \div A + B - C = ($ _____ $)$

/ 4

In each question below, the words can be rearranged to form a sentence. One word doesn't fit in the sentence. Underline the word that doesn't fit.

Example: the morning get I up <u>bed</u> early in

38. apples prefers fruit friend my pears to

39. him rabbit is pet Flopsy called their

40. most place beach favourite the my visit to is

41. we cycled went a weekend bike last ride for

42. wore to danced party my the sequined dress I

43. was me colour I favourite asked my what she

44. and classroom cosy teach the was in warm it

45. wagged tail barked and paws its huge the dog

46. new we show I girl to was around the asked

47. but outside raining was umbrella wanted it to we go

/ 10

The words in the second set follow the same pattern as the words in the first set. Find the missing word to complete the second set.

Example: dose (let) flat   area (___oat___) host

48. pear (rap) real   dull (_____) paid

49. mate (same) sate   tern (_____) dare

50. lean (nil) nail   tube (_____) seen

51. drip (prim) trim   vast (_____) cork

52. flask (tale) slate   pride (_____) tends

53. past (pats) tape   make (_____) road

54. climb (mice) chide   prank (_____) forks

55. mine (nine) nice   claw (_____) best

/ 8

Carry on to the next question → →

Assessment Test 5

Mark two words, one from each set of brackets, that have the most opposite meaning.

Example: (purchase <u>cheap</u> free)   (<u>expensive</u> money bargain)

56. (inferior irrelevant moderate)   (drastic valuable forcible)

57. (anchor mirror compress)   (dissect uproot dissolve)

58. (passionate lethargic impetuous)   (furious scornful apathetic)

59. (slumped uniform deplored)   (languid level exalted)

60. (recklessly bitterly indifferently)   (cowardly gingerly daringly)

61. (proficient shrewd reasonable)   (ungainly incapable graceless)

62. (deplete expend appease)   (undermine weaken provoke)   (/ 7)

Find the number that continues each sequence in the best way.

Example: 3, 5, 7, 9, 11, (_13_)

63. **50, 49, 47, 43, 35, (_____)**

64. **17, 19, 20, 20, 19, 17, (_____)**

65. **15, 17, 20, 25, 32, (_____)**

66. **24, 36, 12, 18, 6, 9, (_____)**

67. **100, 99, 95, 86, (_____)**

68. **96, 96, 48, 16, (_____)**   (/ 6)

Find the letter that will finish the first word and start the second word of each pair. The same letter must be used for both pairs. **Either** mark the letter on the answer sheet, **or** write it on the line.

Example: hol (?) ry   lan (?) oom   _d_

69. fle (?) el   pol (?) lm   (_____)

70. mai (?) ine   ti (?) ip   (_____)

71. vei (?) ook   mea (?) ast   (_____)

72. ja (?) et   ic (?) ap   (_____)

73. bea (?) ite   fil (?) ood   (_____)

74. ai (?) ap   ea (?) ay   (_____)   (/ 6)

Total   / 74

End of Test

Assessment Test 6

Allow 40 minutes to do this test and work as quickly and as carefully as you can.

You can print **multiple-choice answer sheets** for these questions from our website —
go to cgpbooks.co.uk/11plus/answer-sheets or scan the QR code on the right. If you'd
prefer to answer the questions on the page, just follow the instructions in the question.

Answer
Sheets

Read the text carefully and answer the questions that follow.

The Thames Barrier

Flooding is part of London's history: the River Thames is vital for the city's trade and
prosperity, but has caused huge amounts of damage over the centuries. The Thames Barrier
is a flood defence system that stands upriver from central London and protects the city from
dangerous flooding. The decision to erect the barrier was taken following the North Sea Flood
of 1953, when high tide and torrential rain, combined with a powerful storm surge, caused
catastrophic flooding across the city, as well as other parts of the country. In the immediate
aftermath, various flood management measures were discussed, and Sir Hermann Bondi's 1966
independent report strongly recommended that a barrier be built.

Work began in 1974 at a site in Woolwich, south-east London, where the river spans a
width of 520 metres. The barrier was the brainchild of Charles Draper, though many teams of
engineers collaborated on the project during the 8 years between construction starting and the
barrier becoming operational.

The Environment Agency uses information from the Met Office and other sources to
forecast potential flood scenarios up to 36 hours in advance, allowing it to make a decision on
whether the barrier should close. In the first 40 years since its construction, the barrier has
been closed around 200 times, including in 2013-14 when it was closed a record 50 times.

The barrier itself is made up of 10 semi-circular steel gates which span the river. When
the largest of these gates are opened, they move to lying horizontally on the riverbed instead of
standing vertically above the water. To close, the gates rotate 90 degrees to form a solid wall
against the incoming tide, protecting huge swathes of London which include the homes of more
than a million people, the Houses of Parliament and Tower Bridge. The gates can only be raised
just after low tide (a process which takes around 90 minutes). Then, when the water on either
side of the barrier reaches an equal level after high tide, the gates are lowered again, allowing
the water in the river to flow out to sea and ships to pass freely.

The Thames Barrier has been built to contend with the elements and is regularly tested and
carefully maintained. However, the barrier is not just at the mercy of nature; it has been struck
by boats on several occasions. The effectiveness of the barrier's design was demonstrated
in 1997 when a 3000-tonne dredging vessel collided with it: the ship sank and the barrier was
barely damaged.

From the river bank, visitors can see the Thames Barrier in action, and with gates as high
as a 5-storey building when upright, it is a dramatic sight. The Queen has also visited, and
officially opened the barrier a decade after engineers first began building the ambitious structure.
Nowadays, thoughts are turning to the future of the barrier and what will come after it: it was
initially built to last until 2030, although recent analysis has extended its lifespan to 2070.

Carry on to the next question → →

92

> Answer these questions about the text that you've just read.
> Circle the letter of the correct answer.

1. According to the text, why was the decision made to build the Thames Barrier?

    A The city had been hit by its first major flood.
    B The government wanted to protect the Houses of Parliament.
    C Flooding had been getting worse in recent years.
    D The North Sea Flood had caused serious damage to the city.

2. When did the Queen officially open the Thames Barrier?

    A 2 years after it was first in use
    B 8 years after work first began
    C A decade after Charles Draper came up with the idea
    D 30 years after the North Sea Flood

3. According to the text, which of the following statements must be true?

    A The barrier can only remain closed for up to 36 hours.
    B The barrier has been closed an average of 5 times a year since it was built.
    C Some years, the barrier hasn't been closed at all.
    D The barrier has been closed 250 times in total.

4. Who operates the Thames Barrier?

    A Sir Hermann Bondi
    B The Met Office
    C Charles Draper
    D The Environment Agency

5. Why was the barrier barely damaged when a ship struck it in 1997?

    A The ship that hit it was moving slowly.
    B The gates were closed so the ship couldn't get through.
    C The barrier was built to be resilient.
    D The ship sank before it could cause serious damage.

6. Why do you think the Thames Barrier was built in its current location?

    A The river is 520 metres wide at that point.
    B It is upriver from houses and landmarks in central London.
    C The riverbed is flat, allowing ships to pass.
    D The river there is as high as a 5-storey building.

7. According to the text, which of the following statements cannot be true?

    A The barrier's gates are made from metal.
    B The barrier's gates are most often in a horizontal position.
    C The barrier's gates take over an hour to close.
    D The barrier's gates are all identical.

/ 7

8. According to the text, when is the Thames Barrier opened again after being closed?

    A At high tide, when the river is deep enough
    B When the water starts flowing back out to sea
    C When the river is the same height on both sides of the barrier
    D 90 minutes after low tide

9. What do you think happened in 2013-14?

    A Extra maintenance was needed on the barrier.
    B Several ships hit the barrier.
    C The river levels were lower than usual.
    D The weather was particularly stormy.

10. According to the text, which of the following statements is true?

    A A new flood defence will open in 2070.
    B The barrier hasn't been used as much as people thought.
    C The barrier was originally built to last less than 50 years.
    D The existing barrier will close in 2030.

(/ 3)

The number codes for three of these four words are listed in a random order. Work out the code to answer the questions.

REST   **CASE**   **ACTS**   **SEAT**

6143   **2534**   **1635**

11. Find the code for the word **SEAT**.   (_____)

12. Find the code for the word **RACE**.   (_____)

13. Find the word that has the number code **3462**.   (_____)

(/ 3)

Mark the pair of letters that completes each sentence in the most sensible way. Use the alphabet to help you.

A B C D E F G H I J K L M N O P Q R S T U V W X Y Z

Example: BG is to **EJ** as **KP** is to (OS NT <u>NS</u> LO MR).

14. **HJ** is to **DH** as **OT** is to   (KR   PS   PT   KT   PR).

15. **JL** is to **FN** as **PR** is to   (LT   MT   LV   KL   KT).

16. **BY** is to **WF** as **EV** is to   (CD   VD   ZC   CV   ZD).

17. **CG** is to **AL** as **NR** is to   (LM   MW   KV   LW   JW).

18. **AZ** is to **FU** as **GT** is to   (MN   LO   MO   KM   KN).

19. **GR** is to **XE** as **CS** is to   (LF   TG   LG   TK   TF).

(/ 6)

Carry on to the next question → →

Find the word that means the same, or nearly the same, as the word on the left.

Example: stop   begin   <u>halt</u>   start   go

20. **charp**   harmful   astute   cruel   frank

21. **mischief**   jest   hoax   nonsense   devilment

22. **thorough**   unrelenting   entire   passive   conscientious

23. **bound**   encouraged   checked   resolute   compelled

24. **study**   scrutinise   undermine   deduce   criticise

25. **difficult**   unjust   oppressive   pretentious   strenuous

26. **natural**   traditional   inherent   transparent   sincere

27. **skilled**   resourceful   accomplished   innovative   ambitious

/ 8

Each letter stands for a number. Work out the answer to each sum as a letter.

Example: $A = 2$ $B = 3$ $C = 4$ $D = 6$ $E = 8$ $E \div A = (\underline{\ C\ })$

28. $A = 2$ $B = 4$ $C = 8$ $D = 12$ $E = 16$ $E - D + B = (\underline{\hspace{1cm}})$

29. $A = 3$ $B = 6$ $C = 9$ $D = 11$ $E = 22$ $A \times C + B - D = (\underline{\hspace{1cm}})$

30. $A = 2$ $B = 5$ $C = 6$ $D = 10$ $E = 15$ $B \times C \div A - D = (\underline{\hspace{1cm}})$

31. $A = 2$ $B = 4$ $C = 6$ $D = 12$ $E = 18$ $E \div A \times B \div C = (\underline{\hspace{1cm}})$

32. $A = 2$ $B = 8$ $C = 12$ $D = 16$ $E = 24$ $D \div B \times C + A - E = (\underline{\hspace{1cm}})$

/ 5

Find the word that means the opposite, or nearly the opposite, of the word on the left.

Example: large   big   enormous   giant   <u>small</u>

33. **serious**   unwise   frivolous   tense   flexible

34. **limited**   indefinite   partial   crucial   exaggerated

35. **reasoned**   unlikely   thoughtless   predictable   unreliable

36. **reassuring**   overwhelming   surprising   offensive   distressing

37. **premeditated**   doubtful   indecisive   unintentional   undecided

38. **uncomplicated**   intimidating   formidable   introverted   convoluted

39. **disregard**   indifferent   overshadow   acknowledge   interpret

40. **stubborn**   impulsive   friendly   irresolute   vulnerable

/ 8

Circle the letters which correspond to the correct words to complete the passage below.

Hesitantly, I
41. **A** stepped
B step
C stepping
D steps
onto the platform

42. **A** before
B and
C whilst
D however
surveyed the

43. **A** scope
B view
C sighting
D vision
.

My heart pounded,
44. **A** allowed
B prevented
C hindered
D fuelled
by a fear of the unknown. Before

45. **A** retreating
B standing
C leaping
D facing
off the edge,

I felt
46. **A** impressive
B immense
C insincere
D inspiring
excitement

47. **A** secured
B helped
C mingled
D increased
with anticipation

48. **A** for
B when
C then
D as
what I was about to

do. Ziplining had been Lola's idea, with the
49. **A** confusion
B proof
C trust
D intention
of helping me to

50. **A** accomplish
B achieve
C conquer
D perform
my

fear of heights. Before I
51. **A** know
B knew
C known
D knowing
it, I was

52. **A** rising
B delaying
C staying
D soaring
rapidly through the treetops. It was

53. **A** undoubtedly
B unnecessarily
C unsuccessfully
D unimaginatively
the most exhilarating thing I'd ever

54. **A** believed
B delved
C experienced
D imitated
.

/ 14

In each sentence below a four-letter word is hidden at the end of one word and the start of the next. **Either** mark the part of the sentence that contains the hidden word on the answer sheet, **or** write the hidden word on the line.

Example: The large glo<u>be st</u>opped spinning quickly.   (__best__)

55. Everyone celebrated when the feast arrived.   (_____)

56. You must cover your head completely.   (_____)

57. We saw a cute puffin chick.   (_____)

58. The apples plummeted from the tree.   (_____)

59. I am eating sandwiches for lunch.   (_____)

60. Ruben likes putting chilli on food.   (_____)

61. Everyone believes you'll do great things.   (_____)

62. We are meeting later this evening.   (_____)

/ 8

Carry on to the next question → →

Assessment Test 6

Find the three-letter word that completes the word in capital letters, and finishes the sentence in a sensible way.

Example: My family are going on **HOAY** to France. (___LID___)

63. She accidentally **SMED** my favourite mug to pieces. (_____)

64. The postman delivered my **PELS** to the wrong house. (_____)

65. A cat **FOLED** us all the way down the street. (_____)

66. I like to watch the stars **TWLE** at night. (_____)

67. My mum noticed a **PLEM** with the car. (_____)

68. The restaurant only had a small **QUITY** of pizza left. (_____)

69. I **STGLE** to concentrate if I haven't eaten breakfast. (_____)

70. The pigs **GTED** hungrily when we brought them food. (_____)

71. Tyler hasn't stopped **GLING** about beating me at chess. (_____)

72. Julia said she would **CISH** the special gift forever. (_____)

/ 10

Read the information carefully, then use it to answer the question that follows.

73. Fiona, Georgina, Omar, Baljit and Davina took part in a 100 m race.
Baljit won the race in 17 seconds. Fiona was faster than Davina but slower than Georgina.
Georgina crossed the line 3 seconds after Omar, who finished in 19.5 seconds.

If these statements are true, only one of the sentences below **must** be true. Which one?

   A Fiona finished the race in 22.5 seconds.
   B Only Georgina and Baljit were faster than Fiona.
   C Omar crossed the line in third place.
   D Davina came last in the race.
   E Baljit was 3 seconds quicker than Georgina.

74. Jamal, Patrick, Hetty, Rose and Aurianne all went out to buy presents.
Hetty bought 3 presents and spent £15. Rose spent the most money.
Patrick bought the same amount of presents as Hetty and Jamal together.
Aurianne spent £5 less than Patrick, but bought one more present.

If these statements are true, only one of the sentences below **cannot** be true. Which one?

   A Rose spent more money than Jamal.
   B Patrick and Rose bought the same number of presents.
   C Aurianne bought 3 presents.
   D Jamal spent £10.
   E Hetty bought the fewest presents.

/ 2

Total / 74

End of Test

Assessment Test 6

Assessment Test 7

Allow 40 minutes to do this test and work as quickly and as carefully as you can.

You can print **multiple-choice answer sheets** for these questions from our website — go to cgpbooks.co.uk/11plus/answer-sheets or scan the QR code on the right. If you'd prefer to answer the questions on the page, just follow the instructions in the question.

Answer
Sheets

Read this poem carefully and answer the questions that follow.

Vacation

I love the hour before takeoff,
that stretch of no time, no home
but the gray vinyl seats linked like
unfolding paper dolls. Soon we shall
5 be summoned to the gate, soon enough
there'll be the clumsy procedure of row numbers
and perforated stubs — but for now
I can look at these ragtag nuclear families*
with their cooing and bickering
10 or the heeled bachelorette* trying
to ignore a baby's wail and the baby's
exhausted mother waiting to be called up early
while the athlete, one monstrous hand
asleep on his duffel bag, listens,
15 perched like a seal trained for the plunge.

Even the lone executive*
who has wandered this far into summer
with his lasered itinerary, briefcase
knocking his knees — even he
20 has worked for the pleasure of bearing
no more than a scrap of himself
into this hall. He'll dine out, she'll sleep late,
they'll let the sun burn them happy all morning
— a little hope, a little whimsy
25 before the loudspeaker blurts
and we leap up to become
Flight 828, now boarding at Gate 17.

by Rita Dove

*nuclear families — *couples and their children*   *bachelorette — *unmarried woman*
*executive — *businessperson*

Answer these questions about the text that you've just read.
Circle the letter of the correct answer.

1. Which of the following best describes the narrator's experience of flying?

    A They intend never to travel on a plane.
    B They are unfamiliar with how airports work.
    C They have travelled by plane before.
    D They are used to working with planes.

/ 1

2. How is the narrator entertaining themselves while waiting to board their flight?

   A They are remembering previous holidays.
   B They are watching the people around them.
   C They are thinking about their upcoming holiday.
   D They are talking to people nearby.

3. The narrator thinks that going up to the gate is:

   A a stressful process.
   B a boring process.
   C a terrifying process.
   D an awkward process.

4. According to the poem, which of the following characters is likely to board the plane first?

   A The bachelorette
   B The mother with the baby
   C The athlete
   D The executive

5. Which of the following statements is false?

   A The executive has a strict schedule.
   B The executive is on a business trip.
   C The executive is on his own.
   D The executive is carrying a bag.

6. Which of the following is not mentioned in the poem?

   A What the passengers will do on their holidays
   B What time of year it is
   C Where the narrator is travelling to
   D What is announced over the loudspeaker

7. The narrator describes the families as "ragtag" (line 8). This suggests that they:

   A are unruly and disorganised.
   B are prepared to go on their journeys.
   C are being very loud.
   D are moving around the room quickly.

8. Why is the athlete compared to "a seal trained for the plunge" (line 15)?

   A He's nervous about travelling on a plane.
   B He's ready to get up when he's instructed to board.
   C He isn't comfortable where he's sitting.
   D He has a lot of energy and is used to exercising.

/ 7

9. What is meant by the word "summoned" (line 5)?

   A Guided
   B Called
   C Prompted
   D Encouraged

10. What is meant by the word "monstrous" (line 13)?

   A Unusual
   B Heavy
   C Unmoving
   D Colossal

/ 2

Complete the word on the right so that it means the opposite, or nearly the opposite, of the word on the left.

Example: shut   o p e n

11. **jolly** s _ _ _ m n

12. **uplifting** _ r _ g i _

13. **parched** d _ e n _ _ e d

14. **worthless** _ r _ c i _ _ s

15. **tactless** d _ s _ r _ e t

16. **dim** _ _ d i _ n t

17. **secretive** _ o _ t h _ i g _ t

18. **numb** _ _ n s _ t _ v e

19. **inattentive** v _ g _ l a _ t

20. **idle** _ m _ i t _ o _ s

21. **boring** _ i v _ t _ _ g

22. **lasting** f _ _ _ t i n g

/ 12

Carry on to the next question → →

Assessment Test 7

Mark two words, one from each set of brackets, that have the most similar meaning.

Example: (<u>run</u> swim dance)   (walk jump <u>sprint</u>)

23. (positive noble dogged)   (decisive eager tenacious)

24. (equal combine interact)   (cooperate unite discuss)

25. (mock abhor exclude)   (ignore provoke deride)

26. (crowded occupied jostle)   (thick jammed popular)

27. (voyage escort convoy)   (expedition patrol holiday)

/ 5

Find the number that continues each sequence in the best way.

Example: 3, 5, 7, 9, 11, (__13__)

28. **15, 17, 21, 27, 35** (_____)

29. **80, 50, 30, 20, 10,** (_____)

30. **49, 36, 25, 16,** (_____)

31. **4, 5, 8, 17,** (_____)

32. **64, 4, 32, 12, 16, 36,** (_____)

33. **51, 44, 36, 22, 21, 11,** (_____)

/ 6

Mark a word from the first set, followed by a word from the second set, that go together to form a new word.

Example: (care <u>any</u> fly)   (wash wear <u>thing</u>)   (the new word is 'anything')

34. (in hand eye)   (site right tend)

35. (come be hare)   (side bat line)

36. (fact well wit)   (nest or come)

37. (fig lips gull)   (able meant tick)

38. (stun rock thin)   (fell king view)

39. (turn ram add)   (away vice page)

40. (car sins for)   (mat cast ear)

41. (rest pour cove)   (oar red ridge)

/ 8

> The number codes for three of these four words are listed in a random order. Work out the code to answer the questions.

MEAN   LEAD   DALE   MEND

3624   4156   3612

42. Find the code for the word **DALE**.   (_____)

43. Find the code for the word **LAND**.   (_____)

44. Find the word that has the number code **2136**.   (_____)

/ 3

> The number codes for three of these four words are listed in a random order. Work out the code to answer the questions.

TAPS   SOAP   STOP   PUTS

2153   3562   3642

45. Find the code for the word **SOAP**.   (_____)

46. Find the code for the word **POUT**.   (_____)

47. Find the word that has the number code **3612**.   (_____)

48. Find the word that has the number code **2453**.   (_____)

/ 4

> Three of the words in each list are linked. Mark the word that is not related to these three.
>
> **Example:** easy   simple   basic   <u>difficult</u>

49. feather   talon   trotter   beak

50. caption   illustration   paragraph   afterword

51. snowflake   icicle   hailstone   puddle

52. rind   skin   core   peel

53. spiral   revolve   twirl   swing

54. burgundy   indigo   maroon   crimson

55. dock   marina   shoreline   harbour

56. tractor   wagon   carriage   chariot

57. page   leaf   sheet   pamphlet

58. output   formula   recipe   instructions

/ 10

Carry on to the next question → →

Assessment Test 7

Mark the word outside the brackets that has a similar meaning to the words in both sets of brackets.

Example: (travel move)   (turn try)   effort advance attempt <u>go</u> drive

59. (vault treasury)   (hill mound)   safe stock store hoard bank

60. (follow replace)   (achieve win)   triumph result succeed promote accomplish

61. (pact agreement)   (develop catch)   treaty contract incur advance deal

62. (device machine)   (aid reassure)   panel comfort gadget console soothe

63. (intended planned)   (think consider)   deliberate ponder design study arrange

64. (willing likely)   (slanted sloped)   tilted ready inclined tipped keen

65. (decline reject)   (rubbish waste)   spurn refuse foil slump litter

66. (hurt injury)   (crime misdeed)   fault felony injure menace offence

/ 8

Mark the pair of letters that completes each sentence in the most sensible way. Use the alphabet to help you.

A B C D E F G H I J K L M N O P Q R S T U V W X Y Z

Example: BG is to **EJ** as **KP** is to (OS NT <u>NS</u> LO MR).

67. **LV** is to **ST** as **DH** is to   (JF   KJ   KL   LI   KF).

68. **VW** is to **ED** as **LF** is to   (OU   PT   OT   OS   TM).

69. **NP** is to **HU** as **GO** is to   (BU   AS   AT   BT   CS).

70. **MZ** is to **QW** as **AI** is to   (EG   DE   DF   EF   EL).

71. **CU** is to **XF** as **RP** is to   (HK   IK   JL   IJ   JK).

72. **MO** is to **WH** as **DP** is to   (NH   MK   OK   NI   MJ).

73. **QJ** is to **TG** as **SH** is to   (EB   VI   EV   VD   VE).

74. **OR** is to **LI** as **NX** is to   (MD   MC   OD   OM   ML).

/ 8

Total   / 74

End of Test

Assessment Test 8

Allow 40 minutes to do this test and work as quickly and as carefully as you can.

You can print **multiple-choice answer sheets** for these questions from our website —
go to cgpbooks.co.uk/11plus/answer-sheets or scan the QR code on the right. If you'd
prefer to answer the questions on the page, just follow the instructions in the question.

Answer Sheets

> Read this text carefully and answer the questions that follow.

Exploring Empires of Ice

Have you ever wished to visit a fairy-tale castle? Wanted to dive into a world of frozen beauty?

Ice caves are a spectacular natural phenomenon: structures nestled in the hearts of mountains or
glaciers which play host to uniquely exquisite ice formations. Shaped over millennia, these caves are
scattered across the globe, from Argentina to Russia. The Japanese *Narusawa* Ice Cave, for example,
5 is the product of a volcanic eruption over a thousand years ago. In contrast, the man-made cave in
the French *Mer de Glace* glacier has to be carved out anew every year due to the glacier moving.

Unrivalled in its proportions, *Eisriesenwelt* is situated in the Austrian Alps. Despite its magnitude,
the cave remained undiscovered until 1879, when Anton Posselt first ventured into the gloomy
expanse. In the early 20th century, expeditions began in earnest, and explorers gradually revealed
10 the extensive network of glacial tunnels within. Public interest gained pace as the immensity of the
labyrinth came to light, and the earliest tourists visited in the 1920s, clambering up a mountain trail to
reach the cave's entrance.

If you're itching to see this splendour for yourself, sightseers can now access the area in an array
of ways, including bus, train and car. Upon reaching the visitor centre, more intrepid tourists can
15 tackle the arduous climb to the cave's entrance on foot, but people predominantly opt to take the
cable car, which will whisk you up the mountain against a backdrop of breathtaking views.

Once inside, you can delve into a winter wonderland and marvel at the extraordinary ice
formations on display: crystalline columns, glittering stalactites, sheets sparkling like sapphires and
diamonds. Guided tours meander through the magnificent chamber of Posselt Hall, towards Hymir's
20 Castle — a towering sculpture named after a mythological ice giant — and past a composition of
stalactites called the Ice Organ, before culminating in a visit to the Ice Palace, the cave's crowning
glory. After this final stop, you'll return to the entrance and emerge into daylight, cherishing your
memories of the enchanting ice kingdom long after you're warmed by the sun.

> Answer these questions about the text that you've just read.
> Circle the letter of the correct answer.

1. Why do you think the writer begins the text with unanswered questions?

   A The writer wants to interest the reader in ice caves.
   B The writer is unsure if others want to visit somewhere cold.
   C The writer cannot understand how ice caves can be so beautiful.
   D The writer wants to hear the reader's opinion.

/ 1

2. According to the text, what is the highlight of a visit to the *Eisriesenwelt* cave?

   A Posselt Hall
   B Hymir's Castle
   C The Ice Organ
   D The Ice Palace

3. Which of the following statements cannot be true?

   A Posselt Hall is named after the person who found *Eisriesenwelt*.
   B Ice caves often take thousands of years to form.
   C Ice caves are only found in a small region of the world.
   D The *Narusawa* ice cave was formed by a natural disaster.

4. Which of the following statements is true?

   A The tunnels in the *Eisriesenwelt* cave were discovered quickly.
   B Tourists were interested in the ice cave as soon as it was found.
   C There are numerous ways that tourists can travel to *Eisriesenwelt*.
   D The journey in the cable car to the cave takes a long time.

5. What does the text suggest about accessing the *Eisriesenwelt* cave on foot?

   A It is dangerous but popular.
   B It is difficult and daunting.
   C It is feasible but discouraged.
   D It is straightforward and enjoyable.

6. Which of the following statements is false?

   A The *Mer de Glace* glacier moves throughout the year.
   B The *Eisriesenwelt* cave contains many precious gemstones.
   C People have known about the *Eisriesenwelt* cave for over a century.
   D Ice caves can be found inside mountains.

7. Which of the following places is not mentioned as somewhere with natural ice caves?

   A Argentina
   B Japan
   C Russia
   D France

8. According to the text, what is special about the *Eisriesenwelt* cave?

   A It is the biggest ice cave in the world.
   B It was not known about for a long time.
   C It was the first ice cave visited by tourists.
   D It is the only ice cave found in Austria.

   / 7

9. What is meant by the word "phenomenon" (line 2)?

    A Occurrence
    B Impression
    C Exhibition
    D Experience

10. What is meant by the word "predominantly" (line 15)?

    A Authoritatively
    B Principally
    C Seldom
    D Sensibly

/ 2

> Read the information carefully, then use it to answer the question that follows.

11. Rabia, Harvey, Farah, Neave and Dimitris all went to a theme park.

Everyone except Dimitris had a ride on the roller coaster. Four of the children went on the log flume. Rabia is the only child who did not go on the pirate ship ride. Harvey and Dimitris went on the dodgems and the waltzer. Farah did not have a ride on the log flume. Neave and Rabia both went on the ghost train before they had a ride on the roller coaster.

Who went on the **most** rides?   (_____)

12. Lewis, Keira, Ingrid, Quan and Eli are discussing the birds they saw in the school garden.

Four of the children saw a robin in the school garden. Everyone except Lewis spotted a wren. Quan, Keira and Lewis all saw a sparrow, but Ingrid missed the sparrow and the robin because she was looking at the starling. Lewis was the only other child who spotted the starling. Keira and Ingrid were the only children to see a blackbird.

Who spotted the **fewest** birds?   (_____)

/ 2

> Mark two words, one from each set of brackets, that have the most opposite meaning.
>
>   **Example:**   (purchase <u>cheap</u> free)   (<u>expensive</u> money bargain)

13. (smartly pleasantly softly)   (assertively illegally obnoxiously)

14. (confident effective worthwhile)   (apprehensive interrupted chaotic)

15. (deliver trade acquire)   (lease surrender suspend)

16. (concealed unfathomable obscure)   (intelligible sensible profound)

17. (warmth companionship sympathy)   (secrecy solitude desolation)

/ 5

Carry on to the next question → →

Circle the letters which correspond to the correct words to complete the passage below.

Cannons boomed
18. **A** silently
B bitterly
C ferociously
D deafening
the ship
19. **A** pitched
B pitches
C pitching
D pitch
forward, and seconds
20. **A** before
B later
C during
D while
the

pirates were
21. **A** on
B in
C at
D under
board. Susie,
22. **A** smirking
B inflating
C frozen
D quivering
with fear, rolled
23. **A** within
B across
C behind
D until
some barrels

to
24. **A** conceal
B traverse
C expose
D disguise
herself. She
25. **A** should
B can
C would
D could
see a man looming
26. **A** gloomily
B ominously
C sensitively
D brusquely
over her shipmates,

his sword
27. **A** polishing
B holding
C glinting
D bubbling
menacingly in the sunlight. She felt
28. **A** assertive
B harried
C helpless
D sedate
as she heard him

29. **A** raising
B barking
C placing
D proposing
orders at his
30. **A** terrible
B victorious
C mortal
D petrified
prisoners. The situation was
31. **A** fanciful
B perilous
C elusive
D pernicious
: Susie

/ 14

had to do something, and quickly.

Fill in the missing letters to complete the words in the following passage.

32. Stone circles are a type of Stone Age ☐☐ n u ☐ e n t that

33. are found ☐ h r ☐☐ h o u t the British Isles, although they are

34. ☐ a r t ☐☐ l a r l y common in hilly areas. The reasons for

35. their ☐☐ n s t ☐ c t i o n are still unknown. However, there are

36. many theories, including that they were used for ☐☐ l i g ☐☐ u s rituals.

37. Long Meg and Her Daughters is a r e ☐☐ k ☐ b l e stone circle which is the

38. second-largest in England. Long Meg is a huge stone ☐ v e r ☐ o o ☐ i n ☐

39. the circle, which has p r e h ☐☐ t o ☐ c carvings on it. The other stones

40. are referred to as Her Daughters. There are n ☐☐ e ☐☐ u s local

41. legends about the circle, linked to its p ☐ z ☐☐ i ☐ g presence.

/ 10

Assessment Test 8

Remove one letter from the first word and add it to the second word to make two new words. Do not rearrange the other letters. **Either** mark the letter that moves on the answer sheet, **or** write two new words on the lines.

Example: event   hop   (__vent__) (__hope__)

42. proud   for   (_____) (_____)

43. stuck   elf   (_____) (_____)

44. shout   log   (_____) (_____)

45. plain   sun   (_____) (_____)

46. filed   clam   (_____) (_____)

47. chart   font   (_____) (_____)   / 6

Mark two words, one from each set of brackets, that complete the sentence in the most sensible way.

Example: **Eye** is to (face blink <u>see</u>) as **mouth** is to (<u>taste</u> tongue lips).

48. **Hopeful** is to (optimistic auspicious opulent) as **gloomy** is to (faint dismal opaque).

49. **Advice** is to (counsellor kindness guidance) as **warning** is to (caution dislike doubt).

50. **Confirm** is to (prove accept deny) as **agree** is to (interest contradict verify).

51. **Class** is to (pupils academy group) as **regiment** is to (fight army weapon).

52. **Disorder** is to (trouble puzzle chaos) as **organisation** is to (link structure direct).   / 5

The number codes for three of these four words are listed in a random order. Work out the code to answer the questions.

TOUR   STUB   RUST   ROTS

2461   4365   5342

53. Find the code for the word **RUST**.   (_____)

54. Find the code for the word **BOUT**.   (_____)

55. Find the word that has the number code **3624**.   (_____)   / 3

Carry on to the next question → →

Find a word that completes the third pair of words so that it follows the same pattern as the first two pairs.

Example: earn ear   bank ban   seat (___sea___)

56. prefer per   solely sly   online   (_____)

57. alleged leg   control nor   genetic   (_____)

58. pioneer rein   husband daub   herself   (_____)

59. maximum mix   satisfy sit   intense   (_____)

60. meaning gain   element teen   quarter   (_____)

/ 6

Find the letter that will finish the first word and start the second word of each pair. The same letter must be used for both pairs. **Either** mark the letter on the answer sheet, **or** write it on the line.

Example: hol (?) ry   lan (?) oom   ___d___

61. bea (?) ick   spar (?) it   (_____)

62. sur (?) rown   cal (?) und   (_____)

63. fis (?) ow   bu (?) ire   (_____)

64. medi (?) loud   past (?) lone   (_____)

65. for (?) ask   glu (?) rip   (_____)

66. den (?) et   def (?) ear   (_____)

/ 6

Find the word that means the same, or nearly the same, as the word on the left.

Example: stop   begin   <u>halt</u>   start   go

67. **standing**   continuous   progression   celebrity   status

68. **restrain**   provide   curb   conduct   govern

69. **cowardly**   bashful   impudent   craven   gallant

70. **powerfully**   fervently   arrogantly   decidedly   forcibly

71. **increase**   amplify   promote   elaborate   expedite

72. **sullen**   pungent   callous   morose   amiable

73. **regrettable**   disastrous   lamentable   detrimental   prosperous

74. **invention**   observation   fabrication   execution   intuition

/ 8

Total   / 74

End of Test

Glossary

adjective	A word that <u>describes</u> a <u>noun</u>, e.g. '<u>big</u> castle', '<u>yellow</u> flower'.
adverb	A word that <u>describes</u> a <u>verb</u> or an <u>adjective</u>, which often ends with the <u>suffix</u> '<u>-ly</u>', e.g. 'He danced <u>gracefully</u>.', 'She is <u>extremely</u> happy.'
antonym	A word that has the <u>opposite meaning</u> to another word, e.g. the antonym of '<u>bright</u>' is '<u>dark</u>'.
conjunction	A word that <u>joins</u> two clauses, e.g. '<u>and</u>', '<u>but</u>'.
consonants	The <u>21 letters</u> of the alphabet that <u>aren't vowels</u>.
fiction	Text that has been <u>made up</u> by the author, about <u>imaginary people</u> and <u>events</u>.
homographs	Words that are <u>spelt the same</u>, but have <u>different meanings</u>, e.g. 'I heard the dog <u>bark</u>.' and 'The tree <u>bark</u> is covered in flowers.'
homophones	Words that <u>sound the same</u>, but mean different things, e.g. '<u>weak</u>' and '<u>week</u>'.
imagery	Language that creates a <u>vivid picture</u> in the reader's mind.
metaphor	A way of <u>describing</u> something by saying that it <u>is</u> something else, e.g. 'His face was a storm cloud.'
multiple choice	A type of <u>11+ question</u> that gives you <u>answers</u> to choose from.
non-fiction	Text that is about <u>facts</u> and <u>real people</u> and <u>events</u>.
noun	A word that <u>names</u> something, e.g. '<u>Liverpool</u>', '<u>stick</u>', '<u>band</u>', '<u>hope</u>'.
personification	A way of describing something by giving it <u>human feelings</u> and <u>characteristics</u>, e.g. 'The stream babbled merrily as it ran through the woods.'
prefix	Letters that can be put <u>in front</u> of a word to <u>change its meaning</u>, e.g. '<u>dis-</u>' can be added to '<u>appear</u>' to make '<u>disappear</u>'.
pronoun	Words that can be used <u>instead</u> of <u>nouns</u>, e.g. '<u>I</u>', '<u>you</u>', '<u>we</u>', '<u>they</u>'.
simile	A way of describing something by <u>comparing</u> it to something else, e.g. 'We glided through the crowd <u>like</u> boats on the waves.'
subject	The <u>person</u> or <u>thing doing</u> the action of a verb, e.g. '<u>Helena</u> trained.', '<u>The cat</u> purred.'
suffix	Letters that can be put <u>after</u> a word to <u>change its meaning</u>, e.g. '<u>-ness</u>' can be added to the end of '<u>happy</u>' to make '<u>happiness</u>'.
synonym	A word with a <u>similar meaning</u> to another word, e.g. '<u>funny</u>' is a synonym of '<u>amusing</u>'.
verb	An <u>action</u> or <u>being</u> word, e.g. 'I <u>swim</u>', 'she <u>shouted</u>', 'you <u>see</u>'.
vowels	The letters 'a', 'e', 'i', 'o' and 'u'.

Answers

Section One — The Alphabet

Page 2 — Alphabet Positions

1) **J** — J is at position 10 in the alphabet.
2) **P**— P is at position 16 in the alphabet.
3) **V** — V would be at position 5.
4) **G** — G would be at position 20.
5) **19** — S is at position 19 in the alphabet.
6) **14** — N is at position 14 in the alphabet.
7) **5** — E is the middle letter and is at position 5 in the alphabet.
8) **12** — L is the middle letter and is at position 12 in the alphabet.
9) **K** — K would be at position 7.
10) **11** — Q would be at position 11.
11) **4** — F would be at position 4.
12) **15** — V would be at position 15.

Page 3 — Identify a Letter from a Clue

1) **R** — R is the only letter that occurs once in TREEHOUSE and twice in TOMORROW.
2) **C**— C is the only letter that occurs three times in ECCENTRICITY.
3) **L** — L is the letter that occurs most often in COLLECTIBLE.
4) **N** — N is the letter that occurs most often in ENVIRONMENTS.
5) **A** — A is the letter that occurs most often in PARAPHRASES.
6) **G** — G is the only letter that occurs once in ELIGIBLE and twice in BEGRUDGE.
7) **I** — I is the only letter that occurs once in LIMPETS, twice in FINISHES and three times in ACTIVITIES.
8) **S** — S is the letter that appears most often in FESTIVALS, SAUSAGES and DISCUSSED.
9) **T** — T is the only letter that appears twice in PRESENTATION and twice in CRITTERS.
10) **L** — L is the only letter that appears once in DELIRIUM and once in DISMANTLE, but not in DIAMETER.
11) **E** — E is the only letter that appears twice in SEMICIRCLE, twice in SEMIPRECIOUS and three times in SEMIRETIRED.
12) **A** — A is the only letter that appears twice in CATERPILLAR, twice in RECTANGULAR and once in TEACUPS.
13) **H** — H is the only letter that appears once in ENTHUSIASTIC, once in SUNDRENCHED and twice in HONEYBUNCH.
14) **M** — M is the only letter that appears twice in MANAGEMENT, twice in UNEMPLOYMENT and once in MALICIOUS.

Page 4 — Alphabetical Order

1) **pineapple** — The words go in the order 'pianist', 'piggybacked', 'pineapple', 'pistachio', 'pitchfork'.
2) **mishandled** — The words go in the order 'miscellaneous', 'mischief', 'mishandled', 'missiles', 'mistake'.
3) **antonym** — The words go in the order 'antelopes', 'anthropology', 'antiquated', 'antonym'.

4) **destination** — The words go in the order 'descent', 'deserted', 'despondent', 'dessert', 'destination'.
5) **S** — S is the letter that comes last in the alphabet.
6) **G** — G is the letter that comes first in the alphabet.
7) **D** — D is the letter that comes first in the alphabet.
8) **U** — U is the letter that comes last in the alphabet.
9) **comprehension** — The words go in the order 'expulsion', 'comprehension', 'aspersion', 'percussion'.
10) **robbery** — The words go in the order 'granary', 'robbery', 'trickery', 'bravery', 'enquiry'.
11) **resemble** — The words go in the order 'stable', 'convertible', 'shamble', 'resemble', 'crumble'.
12) **mystify** — The words go in the order 'specify', 'humidify', 'disqualify', 'mystify', 'satisfy'.

Section Two — Spelling and Grammar

Page 5 — Plurals

1) **spies** — 'spy' becomes 'spies' — words ending in a consonant and 'y' lose the final 'y' and add 'ies' to make the plural.
2) **hooves** — 'hoof' becomes 'hooves' — often words ending in 'f' lose the final 'f' and add 'ves' to make the plural.
3) **reefs** — 'reef' becomes 'reefs' — this is different to most words ending in 'f' because only 's' is added to make the plural.
4) **peaches** — 'peach' becomes 'peaches' — often words ending in 'ch' add 'es' to make the plural.
5) **tornadoes** — 'tornado' becomes 'tornadoes' — some words ending in 'o' add 'es' to make the plural.
6) **studios** — 'studio' becomes 'studios' — some words ending in 'o' add 's' to make the plural.
7) **leaves** — 'leaf' becomes 'leaves' — often words ending in 'f' lose the final 'f' and add 'ves' to make the plural.
8) **echoes** — 'echo' becomes 'echoes' — some words ending in 'o' add 'es' to make the plural.
9) **scuffs** — 'scuff' becomes 'scuffs' — words ending in 'ff' add 's' to make the plural.
10) **geese** — 'goose' becomes 'geese' — this is an irregular plural.
11) **fishermen** — 'fisherman' becomes 'fishermen' — this is an irregular plural.
12) **teeth** — 'tooth' becomes 'teeth' — this is an irregular plural.
13) **lice** — 'louse' becomes 'lice' — this is an irregular plural.
14) **offspring** — 'offspring' does not change — this is an irregular plural.
15) **species** — 'species' does not change — this is an irregular plural.
16) **diagnoses** — 'diagnosis' becomes 'diagnoses' — this is an irregular plural.
17) **fungi** — 'fungus' becomes 'fungi' — this is an irregular plural.
18) **ellipses** — 'ellipsis' becomes 'ellipses' — this is an irregular plural.

Page 6 — Homophones

1) **lynx** — 'lynx' makes sense here — it is a type of wildcat found in Canada, whereas 'links' means 'joins together'.

2) **gate** — 'gate' makes sense here — it is a barrier that can be opened and closed, whereas 'gait' describes the way someone walks.

3) **bold** — 'bold' makes sense here — it is the word used to describe text which is darker and thicker than normal, whereas 'bowled' means 'rolled'.

4) **pane** — 'pane' makes sense here — it is the word for a sheet of glass that fills a window frame, whereas 'pain' describes the feeling of being hurt.

5) **cruise** — 'cruise' makes sense here — it is the word for a type of holiday taken by boat, whereas 'crews' is a word for groups of people who work together.

6) **arc** — 'arc' makes sense here — it is a semi-circular shape, whereas an 'ark' is a type of boat.

7) **wrung** — 'wrung' makes sense here — it means 'squeezed tightly', whereas 'rung' means 'called on the phone'.

8) **feat** — 'feat' makes sense here — it means 'achievement', whereas 'feet' are a body part.

9) **lapse** — 'lapse' makes sense here — it is a word used to describe a temporary failure, whereas 'laps' are circuits of a track or swimming pool.

10) **pour** — 'pour' makes sense here — it is a word to describe the action of moving a liquid from one container to another, whereas 'poor' means 'lacking money', and a 'pore' is a tiny hole in a person's skin .

11) **seize** — 'seize' makes sense here — it means 'take forcefully', whereas 'seas' are bodies of water, and 'sees' means 'views'.

12) **You're** — 'You're' makes sense here — it is a shortened version of 'You are', whereas 'Your' means 'belonging to you', and 'Yore' means 'a long time ago'.

13) **towed** — 'towed' makes sense here — it means 'pulled along', whereas a 'toad' is a frog-like animal, and 'toed' means 'touched with your toes'.

14) **aisle** — 'aisle' makes sense here — it is the word for a gap between rows of seats, whereas 'isle' is a shortened form of the word 'island', and 'I'll' is short for 'I will'.

15) **wail** — 'wail' makes sense here — it is a word for the sound you make when you are in pain, whereas a 'wale' is a streak or ridge, and a 'whale' is a type of marine mammal.

16) **by** — 'by' makes sense here — it completes the phrase 'close by', whereas 'bye' is short for 'goodbye', and 'buy' means 'purchase'.

17) **Their** — 'Their' makes sense here — it means 'belonging to them', whereas 'They're' is short for 'They are', and 'There' means 'in that place'.

18) **site** — 'site' makes sense here — it is a word used to describe a place or location, whereas 'cite' means 'to refer to', and 'sight' is the act of seeing.

Page 7 — Prefixes and Suffixes

1) **pre** — the word is 'preorder'.

2) **sub** — the word is 'subtitles'.

3) **re** — the word is 'repaint'.

4) **un** — the word is 'unlikely'.

5) **sub** — the word is 'subtotal'.

6) **im** — the word is 'improbable'.

7) **un** — the word is 'unprofessional'.

8) **re** — the word is 'replayed'.

9) **de** — the word is 'dehydrated'.

10) **membership** — the suffix added is 'ship'.

11) **glorious** — the suffix added is 'ous', but you also need to change the 'y' in 'glory' to an 'i' — this is quite common for words ending in 'y'.

12) **impressive** — the suffix added is 'ive'.

13) **weakness** — the suffix added is 'ness'.

14) **tasteless** — the suffix added is 'less'.

15) **successful** — the suffix added is 'ful'.

16) **animation** — the suffix added is 'ion' but you also need to remove the 'e' from 'animate'.

17) **reliable** — the suffix added is 'able', but you also need to change the 'y' in 'rely' to an 'i' — this is quite common for words ending in 'y'.

18) **achievement** — the suffix added is 'ment'.

Page 8 — Awkward Spellings

1) **i o** — The sentence is 'Hayley was eas*i*ly the strongest swimmer in her age categ*o*ry.'

2) **i e** — The sentence is 'The bus*i*ness was charged a high rate of int*e*rest by the bank.'

3) **a e** — The sentence is 'Carl was miser*a*ble at the thought of eating all his veg*e*tables.'

4) **e e** — The sentence is 'Ashni was confident that she had good g*e*neral knowl*e*dge.'

5) **a a** — The sentence is 'The builders argued over the bound*a*ry of the priv*a*te driveway.'

6) **a e** — The sentence is 'Mrs Dornan gave her secret*a*ry a good ref*e*rence when she got a new job.'

7) **i a** — The sentence is 'Punam was respons*i*ble for volunt*a*ry work at her local animal shelter.'

8) **a o** — The sentence is 'The origin*a*l plans for the new shopping centre had to be aband*o*ned.'

9) **e a** — The sentence is 'There are many ben*e*fits to walking compared to being sedent*a*ry.'

10) **wr dd** — The sentence is 'Niamh had *wr*itten her sister's new a*dd*ress on the envelope.'

11) **gn pp** — The sentence is 'The garden *gn*ome had to*pp*led over in the bad weather.'

12) **pp ch** — The sentence is 'Suyin ha*pp*ily played several *ch*ords on the piano.'

13) **rr ff** — The sentence is 'Otis was late to the party because of the te*rr*ible tra*ff*ic.'

14) **dd pp** — The sentence is 'Mrs Brown shu*dd*ered when she saw all the sweet wra*pp*ers in the bin.'

15) **rr sc** — The sentence is 'The runner was i*rr*itated that he had pulled a mu*sc*le in his leg.'

16) **bt ss** — The sentence is 'John dou*bt*ed that he would finish his e*ss*ay by the deadline.'

17) **ss lk** — The sentence is 'The de*ss*ert was made from a mixture of sugar, flour, butter and egg yo*lk*s.'

18) **lm pp** — The sentence is 'Simon usually likes eating sa*lm*on, but today he's lost his a*pp*etite.'

Page 9 — Mixed Spelling Questions

1) **giraffes** — 'giraffs' should be 'giraffes' — the 'e' is not removed in the plural.
2) **stalk** — 'stork' should be 'stalk' — 'stalk' is the correct homophone to use in this sentence.
3) **pressure** — 'presure' should be 'pressure' — it contains a double 's'.
4) **irrational** — 'irational' should be 'irrational' — when the 'ir' prefix is added, the root word keeps its initial 'r'.
5) **informal** — 'informul' should be 'informal' — it ends in 'al'.
6) **mowed** — 'mode' should be 'mowed' — 'mowed' is the correct homophone to use in this sentence.
7) **neighbours** — 'nieghbours' should be 'neighbours' — it has an 'ei' in the middle. It follows the rule "i before 'e' except after 'c', but only when it rhymes with 'bee'."
8) **infectious** — 'infectous' should be 'infectious' — it ends in 'ious'.
9) **memorable** — 'memerable' should be 'memorable' — the root word is 'memory'.
10) **poisonous** — 'poisunous' should be 'poisonous' — the root word is 'poison'.
11) **policies** — 'policys' should be 'policies' — the 'y' changes to an 'i' when 'es' is added to make the plural.
12) **wreckage** — 'reckage' should be 'wreckage' — it starts with a silent 'w'.
13) **deceive** — 'decieve' should be 'deceive' — it has an 'ei' in the middle. It follows the rule "i before 'e' except after 'c', but only when it rhymes with 'bee'."
14) **fascinated** — 'fasinated' should be 'fascinated' — it has a silent 'c' in the middle.
15) **According** — 'Acording' should be 'According' — it has a double 'c'.
16) **incomplete** — 'imcomplete' should be 'incomplete' — the correct prefix to add is 'in'.
17) **edition** — 'editian' should be 'edition' — the correct suffix to add is 'ion'.
18) **interruption** — 'interuption' should be 'interruption' — the root word is 'interrupt'.

Page 10 — Mixed Spelling Questions

1) **currents** — 'currents' makes sense here because it means 'moving water'.
2) **currants** — 'currants' makes sense here because it means 'small dried fruit'.
3) **accept** — 'accept' makes sense here because it is a verb which means 'to believe or recognise'.
4) **except** — 'except' makes sense here because it means 'not including'.
5) **stationery** — 'stationery' makes sense here because it means 'writing equipment'.
6) **stationary** — 'stationary' makes sense here because it means 'not moving'.
7) **practise** — 'practise' makes sense here because it is a verb in this sentence.
8) **practice** — 'practice' makes sense here because it is a noun in this sentence.
9) **lose** — 'lose' makes sense here because it is a verb that means 'to misplace'.
10) **loose** — 'loose' makes sense here because it is an adjective that means 'unfastened'.

11) **borrow** — 'borrow' makes sense here because it means 'to take something you intend to return'.
12) **lend** — 'lend' makes sense here because it means 'to give something with the intention of it being returned'.
13) **aloud** — 'aloud' makes sense here because it means 'loud enough to hear'.
14) **allowed** — 'allowed' makes sense here because it means 'to be permitted to'.
15) **ensure** — 'ensure' makes sense here because it means 'to check and be certain'.
16) **insure** — 'insure' makes sense here because it means 'to pay to protect'.
17) **effect** — 'effect' makes sense here because it is a noun in this sentence.
18) **affect** — 'affect' makes sense here because it is a verb in this sentence.

Page 11 — Verbs

1) **The sheep** — 'The sheep' is the subject in this sentence because it is doing the action — 'The sheep leapt'.
2) **showed** — 'showed' is the verb in this sentence because it is the action word.
3) **Reuben** — 'Reuben' is the subject in this sentence because he is doing the action — 'Reuben was singing'.
4) **shone** — 'shone' is the verb in this sentence because it is the action word.
5) **Mr Clarke** — 'Mr Clarke' is the subject in this sentence because he is doing the action — 'Mr Clarke passed'.
6) **Parv and Jamie** — 'Parv and Jamie' are the subject in this sentence because they are doing the action — 'Parv and Jamie watched'.
7) **echoes** — 'echoes' is the verb in this sentence because it is the action word.
8) **glanced** — 'glanced' is the verb in this sentence because it is the action word.
9) **Swimming** — 'Swimming' is the subject in this sentence because it is doing the action — 'Swimming is'.
10) **did** — The sentence should be 'Before the race started, the runner did some final stretches.' This is the correct past tense form of the verb 'to do' and agrees with the subject — 'the runner'.
11) **Go** — The sentence should be 'Go through the gate, then turn right at the farm.' This is an instruction, and 'Go' is the correct option in the imperative.
12) **drives** — The sentence should be 'Emma drives slowly when she is nervous.' The sentence is in the present tense so 'drives' is correct.
13) **are** — The sentence should be 'The sunflowers that Abigail planted are growing very tall.' This completes the verb phrase 'are growing' and agrees with the subject of the verb — 'The sunflowers'.
14) **explain** — The sentence should be 'It's crucial that we explain these sales figures.' The sentence uses the subjunctive form, so 'explain' is the correct option.
15) **ate** — The sentence should be 'Mrs Gomez ate her salad and took a sip of water.' The sentence is in the past tense so 'ate' is correct.
16) **were** — The sentence should be 'If I were you, I would see a doctor soon.' The sentence is about a situation that isn't real, so the subjunctive 'were' is correct.
17) **rung** — The sentence should be 'Janek had rung the doorbell three times.' This completes the verb phrase 'had rung'.

18) given — The sentence should be 'I will be <u>given</u> my timetable on the first day of school.' The sentence is in the future tense, but this completes the verb phrase 'will be given'.

Page 12 — Verbs and Conjunctions

1) forgave — The sentence should be 'Aleksy forgave his sister when she broke his toy.' This is the correct past tense form of the verb 'to forgive'.

2) hidden — The sentence should be 'The cat has hidden my scarf and I can't find it.' This is the correct word to complete the verb phrase 'has hidden'.

3) was (or **had been**) — The sentence should be 'Last year, Ewan was a regular member of chess club.' This is the correct past tense form of the verb 'to be'.

4) knew — The sentence should be 'If you knew the answer, why didn't you say so?' This is the correct past tense form of the verb 'to know'.

5) go — The sentence should be 'When the bell rings, go inside and be quiet!' The sentence is an instruction, and this is the correct imperative form of the verb 'to go'.

6) get — The sentence should be 'I will get you a jumper if you feel cold.' This is the correct future tense form of the verb 'to get'.

7) found — The sentence should be 'Tamsin was walking through the park when she found the money.' This is the correct past tense form of the verb 'to find'.

8) writing (or **going to write**)— The sentence should be 'The teacher is writing on the board while the pupils read.' This is the correct word to complete the verb phrase 'is writing'.

9) flies — The sentence should be 'Jim always flies first class when he travels for work.' This is the correct present tense form of the verb 'to fly'.

10) when — 'when' makes the most sense in this sentence.

11) because — 'because' makes the most sense in this sentence.

12) whereas — 'whereas' makes the most sense in this sentence.

13) so — 'so' makes the most sense in this sentence.

14) if — 'if' makes the most sense in this sentence.

15) unless — 'unless' makes the most sense in this sentence.

16) and — 'and' makes the most sense in this sentence.

17) before — 'before' makes the most sense in this sentence.

18) although — 'although' makes the most sense in this sentence.

Page 13 — Mixed Grammar Questions

1) elderly — 'elderly' is the adjective in this sentence. It describes the noun 'gentleman'.

2) cows — 'cows' is the common noun in this sentence. A common noun is a naming word for general things.

3) drifted — 'drifted' is the verb in this sentence. A verb is a doing or being word.

4) wondered — 'wondered' is the verb in this sentence. A verb is a doing or being word.

5) badly — 'badly' is the adverb in this sentence. It describes the verb 'ended'.

6) before — 'before' is the conjunction in this sentence. A conjunction joins sentences or clauses together.

7) Anna — 'Anna' is the proper noun in this sentence. Proper nouns name specific people, places and things.

8) almost — 'almost' is the adverb in this sentence. It describes the verb 'smell'.

9) challenging — 'challenging' is the adjective in this sentence. It describes the noun 'the questions'.

10) theirs — 'their' should be 'theirs'.

11) any — 'no' should be 'any'.

12) were — 'was' should be 'were'.

13) turn — 'turns' should be 'turn'.

14) attend — 'attends' should be 'attend'.

15) well — 'good' should be 'well'.

16) I — 'me' should be 'I'.

17) broken — 'broke' should be 'broken'.

18) that (or **which**) — 'what' should be 'that' or 'which'.

Page 14 — Mixed Grammar Questions

1) cross — The sentence should be 'I told Max not to <u>cross</u> the road without me.' This completes the verb phrase 'told Max not to cross'.

2) harder — The sentence should be 'Helen works <u>harder</u> than anyone else I know.' This is the correct option to complete the comparison 'harder than'.

3) drink — The sentence should be 'Don't <u>drink</u> my coffee before I get back!' This completes the verb phrase 'Don't drink'.

4) mine — The sentence should be 'I couldn't believe that the winning ticket was <u>mine</u>.' This is the correct possessive pronoun to complete this sentence.

5) since — The sentence should be 'My favourite jumper has stretched <u>since</u> you borrowed it.' This is the correct conjunction to complete this sentence.

6) sleep — The sentence should be 'If I ate healthier food, I would <u>sleep</u> better.' This completes the verb phrase 'would sleep'.

7) torn — The sentence should be 'My jacket was <u>torn</u> by the barbed wire fence.' This completes the verb phrase 'was torn'.

8) which — The sentence should be 'I repeated the number <u>which</u> they had given me.' This is the correct option to complete this sentence.

9) before — The sentence should be 'Can we find them <u>before</u> it gets dark?' This is the correct conjunction to complete this sentence.

10) wakes — The sentence should be 'Theo <u>wakes</u> early and dresses quietly.' This is the correct present tense form of the verb 'to wake'.

11) be — The sentence should be 'You can't <u>be</u> serious about going out in that rain.' This is the completes the verb phrase 'can't be'.

12) work — The sentence should be 'It is important that you <u>work</u> in the family shop.' This sentence uses the subjunctive form, so 'work' is the correct option.

13) many — The sentence should be 'There are too <u>many</u> plates on the table.' This is the correct option to complete this sentence.

14) Buy — The sentence should be '<u>Buy</u> these boots — now half price!' The sentence is a command and this is the correct option in the imperative.

15) ours — The sentence should be 'The trophy is <u>ours</u> because we won the tournament.' This is the correct possessive pronoun to complete this sentence.

16) chooses — The sentence should be 'Ryan <u>chooses</u> apple pie every time we come here.' The sentence is in the present tense, so this is the correct option.

17) quickly — The sentence should be 'The water <u>quickly</u> reached our front door.' This is the correct adverb to complete this sentence.

18) but — The sentence should be 'We saw llamas on our walk, <u>but</u> they were sleeping.' This is the correct option to complete this sentence.

Section Three — Making Words

Page 15 — Missing Letters

1) **e** — The new words are 'wise', 'eat', 'pace' and 'earn'.
2) **a** — The new words are 'gala', 'away', 'data' and 'arid'.
3) **w** — The new words are 'drew', 'wand', 'snow' and 'wasp'.
4) **l** — The new words are 'wool', 'lend', 'gel' and 'live'.
5) **r** — The new words are 'soar', 'rust', 'stir' and 'rare'.
6) **k** — The new words are 'link', 'kid', 'weak' and 'kept'.
7) **n** — The new words are 'skin', 'none', 'bean' and 'newt'.
8) **g** — The new words are 'twig', 'glum', 'pig' and 'gave'.
9) **t** — The new words are 'out', 'tide', 'net' and 'tie'.
10) **f** — The new words are 'golf', 'five', 'half' and 'fit'.
11) **s** — The new words are 'moss', 'sake', 'bus' and 'slot'.
12) **l** — The new words are 'fell', 'look', 'owl' and 'lid'.
13) **m** — The new words are 'ham', 'mice', 'aim' and 'mist'.
14) **y** — The new words are 'tray', 'year', 'any' and 'yard'.
15) **f** — The new words are 'beef', 'fade', 'elf' and 'fir'.
16) **p** — The new words are 'hip', 'peek', 'nip' and 'prey'.
17) **w** — The new words are 'saw', 'wry', 'stew' and 'warm'.
18) **l** — The new words are 'call', 'lace', 'fail' and 'low'.
19) **b** — The new words are 'tub', 'bid', 'comb' and 'bolt'.
20) **w** — The new words are 'mow', 'wail', 'claw' and 'wait'.

Page 16 — Move a Letter

1) **p** — The new words are 'late' and 'beep'.
2) **r** — The new words are 'make' and 'rant'.
3) **l** — The new words are 'idea' and 'bowl'.
4) **w** — The new words are 'hose' and 'wash'.
5) **t** — The new words are 'here' and 'tent'.
6) **r** — The new words are 'fist' and 'ever'.
7) **h** — The new words are 'fort' and 'hill'.
8) **f** — The new words are 'lash' and 'left'.
9) **e** — The new words are 'blow' and 'site'.
10) **u** — The new words are 'bond' and 'fury'.
11) **i** — The new words are 'gong' and 'main'.
12) **t** — The new words are 'rack' and 'told'.
13) **w** — The new words are 'sift' and 'sway'.
14) **r** — The new words are 'cave' and 'port'.
15) **b** — The new words are 'fire' and 'bred'.
16) **a** — The new words are 'cost' and 'stay'.
17) **d** — The new words are 'crow' and 'lady'.
18) **n** — The new words are 'rage' and 'wing'.
19) **o** — The new words are 'slid' and 'soon'.
20) **a** — The new words are 'void' and 'lead'.

Page 17 — Hidden Word

1) **sofa irritates** — The hidden word is 'fair'.
2) **stash old** — The hidden word is 'hold'.
3) **backfired on** — The hidden word is 'redo'.
4) **Children tend** — The hidden word is 'rent'.
5) **cannot explain** — The hidden word is 'note'.
6) **slope nearby** — The hidden word is 'open'.
7) **sweep almonds** — The hidden word is 'palm'.
8) **council acknowledged** — The hidden word is 'lack'.
9) **famous avenue** — The hidden word is 'save'.
10) **kitten doesn't** — The hidden word is 'tend'.
11) **pasta skilfully** — The hidden word is 'task'.
12) **goat ourselves** — The hidden word is 'tour'.
13) **cobra blends** — The hidden word is 'able'.
14) **twenty people** — The hidden word is 'type'.
15) **group only** — The hidden word is 'upon'.
16) **umbrella kept** — The hidden word is 'lake'.
17) **help lottery** — The hidden word is 'plot'.
18) **music opened** — The hidden word is 'cope'.
19) **polo anymore** — The hidden word is 'loan'.
20) **invite many** — The hidden word is 'item'.

Page 18 — Find the Missing Word

1) **ARE** — The complete word is PARENTS.
2) **LIE** — The complete word is RELIEF.
3) **PAN** — The complete word is COMPANY.
4) **LET** — The complete word is ATHLETIC.
5) **PEA** — The complete word is APPEAR.
6) **ACT** — The complete word is FACTORY.
7) **CAT** — The complete word is INDICATED.
8) **EAR** — The complete word is CLEARING.
9) **AGE** — The complete word is PAGES.
10) **EAT** — The complete word is CREATIVE.
11) **RIB** — The complete word is TERRIBLE.
12) **SUM** — The complete word is ASSUMED.
13) **RID** — The complete word is BRIDGE.
14) **ATE** — The complete word is STRATEGY.
15) **ART** — The complete word is PARTNERS.
16) **HER** — The complete word is NOWHERE.
17) **DEN** — The complete word is TENDENCY.
18) **RAM** — The complete word is CARAMEL.
19) **FOR** — The complete word is EFFORT.
20) **DIN** — The complete word is ORDINARY.

Page 19 — Use a Rule to Make a Word

1) **ear** — Take letter 4 from the first word, followed by letter 3 from the second word, and then letter 3 from the first word.
2) **top** — Take letters 3 and 2 from the second word, followed by letter 4 from the first word.
3) **held** — Take letters 1 and 4 from the second word, followed by letters 3 and 4 from the first word.
4) **who** — Take letter 2 from the second word, followed by letters 1 and 2 from the first word.
5) **has** — Take letter 2 from the first word, letter 2 from the second word, and then letter 1 from the first word.
6) **gem** — Take letter 4 from the second word, followed by letters 4 and 1 from the first word.
7) **ate** — Take letter 2 from the first word, followed by letter 1 from the second word, and then letter 4 from the first word.
8) **rid** — Take letter 1 from the first word, followed by letters 2 and 4 from the second word.
9) **ice** — Take letters 3 and 1 from the second word, followed by letter 2 from the first word.
10) **bald** — Take letters 2, 1 and 3 from the second word, followed by letter 4 from the first word.
11) **dent** — Take letter 4 from the first word, followed by letter 4 from the second word, followed by letter 3 from the first word, and then letter 1 from the second word.
12) **deep** — Take letter 4 from the first word, followed by letter 3 from the second word, followed by letter 2 from the first word, and then letter 1 from the second word.
13) **flat** — Take letter 3 from the second word, followed by letters 3 and 1 from the first word, and then letter 4 from the second word.
14) **rare** — Take letters 4 and 3 from the second word, followed by letter 1 from the first word, and then letter 2 from the second word.
15) **nod** — Take letter 2 from the first word, followed by letters 2 and 1 from the second word.
16) **bold** — Take letter 4 from the first word, followed by letter 2 from the second word, followed by letter 2 from the first word, and then letter 1 from the second word.
17) **gram** — Take letter 4 from the second word, followed by letters 2, 1 and 3 from the first word.
18) **role** — Take letters 4 and 2 from the first word, followed by letters 2 and 3 from the second word.
19) **liar** — Take letters 3, 4 and 2 from the first word, followed by letter 3 from the second word.
20) **heir** — Take letter 4 from the second word, followed by letter 4 from the first word, followed by letter 2 from the second word, and then letter 1 from the first word.

Page 20 — Compound Words

1) **keyboard** — 'keyboard' is the only correctly spelled word that can be made.
2) **ponytail** — 'ponytail' is the only correctly spelled word that can be made.
3) **bookmark** — 'bookmark' is the only correctly spelled word that can be made.
4) **homemade** — 'homemade' is the only correctly spelled word that can be made.
5) **backpack** — 'backpack' is the only correctly spelled word that can be made.
6) **nobody** — 'nobody' is the only correctly spelled word that can be made.

7) **weekend** — 'weekend' is the only correctly spelled word that can be made.
8) **countdown** — 'countdown' is the only correctly spelled word that can be made.
9) **fortune** — 'fortune' is the only correctly spelled word that can be made.
10) **shortage** — 'shortage' is the only correctly spelled word that can be made.
11) **overcome** — 'overcome' is the only correctly spelled word that can be made.
12) **wildlife** — 'wildlife' is the only correctly spelled word that can be made.
13) **island** — 'island' is the only correctly spelled word that can be made.
14) **hidden** — 'hidden' is the only correctly spelled word that can be made.
15) **notice** — 'notice' is the only correctly spelled word that can be made.
16) **legend** — 'legend' is the only correctly spelled word that can be made.
17) **likewise** — 'likewise' is the only correctly spelled word that can be made.
18) **behalf** — 'behalf' is the only correctly spelled word that can be made.
19) **pleasure** — 'pleasure' is the only correctly spelled word that can be made.
20) **domain** — 'domain' is the only correctly spelled word that can be made.

Page 21 — Forming New Words

1) **day** — The new words are 'daytime', 'daydream' and 'daylight'.
2) **honey** — The new words are 'honeymoon', 'honeycomb' and 'honeybee'.
3) **foot** — The new words are 'foothold', 'footrest' and 'footpath'.
4) **in** — The new words are 'indoors', 'infuse' and 'income'.
5) **life** — The new words are 'lifeguard', 'lifeboat' and 'lifetime'.
6) **short** — The new words are 'shortcut', 'shortbread' and 'shortlist'.
7) **man** — The new words are 'manhole', 'mankind' and 'manhunt'.
8) **birth** — The new words are 'birthday', 'birthmark' and 'birthplace'.
9) **fall** — The new words are 'downfall', 'snowfall' and 'waterfall'.
10) **hand** — The new words are 'secondhand', 'backhand' and 'beforehand'.
11) **ground** — The new words are 'fairground', 'campground' and 'battleground'.
12) **work** — The new words are 'framework', 'patchwork' and 'paperwork'.
13) **keeper** — The new words are 'goalkeeper', 'innkeeper' and 'housekeeper'.
14) **power** — The new words are 'brainpower', 'manpower' and 'willpower'.
15) **tight** — The new words are 'airtight', 'watertight' and 'skintight'.
16) **down** — The new words are 'rundown', 'meltdown' and 'showdown'.

Page 22 — Complete a Word Pair

1) **bend** — Replace the letter 'a' with the letter 'e'.
2) **hear** — Rearrange letters 1, 2, 3, 5 in the order 5, 1, 2, 3.
3) **vein** — Rearrange letters 1, 2, 3, 4 in the order 3, 4, 1, 2.
4) **see** — Rearrange letters 2, 3, 5 in the order 5, 2, 3.
5) **awe** — Remove letters 2, 3 and 6, leaving the remaining letters in the order 1, 4, 5.
6) **stops** — Rearrange letters 1, 2, 3, 4, 5 in the order 5, 4, 3, 2, 1.
7) **trip** — Rearrange letters 1, 2, 3, 5 in the order 5, 2, 3, 1.
8) **meat** — Rearrange letters 2, 4, 5, 6 in the order 6, 4, 5, 2.
9) **seal** — Rearrange letters 2, 3, 4, 5 in the order 4, 5, 2, 3.
10) **main** — The last letter of the word moves forward two places along the alphabet.
11) **tree** — Rearrange letters 1, 3, 5, 6 in the order 3, 5, 6, 1.
12) **icon** — Rearrange letters 1, 2, 3, 4 in the order 1, 3, 4, 2.
13) **wets** — Rearrange letters 1, 2, 4, 5 in the order 2, 4, 5, 1.
14) **year** — Rearrange letters 3, 4, 5, 6 in the order 4, 5, 3, 6.
15) **path** — Rearrange letters 2, 3, 4, 5 in the order 4, 3, 5, 2.
16) **seek** — The first letter of the word moves backwards 4 places along the alphabet.
17) **day** — Rearrange letters 1, 3, 6 in the order 6, 1, 3.
18) **rat** — Rearrange letters 4, 6, 7 in the order 7, 6, 4.
19) **art** — Rearrange letters 4, 5, 6 in the order 6, 4, 5.
20) **pen** — Rearrange letters 3, 5, 7 in the order 3, 7, 5.

Page 23 — Anagram in a Sentence

1) **BIRD** — BIRD is the only correctly spelled word that fits the sentence.
2) **SPEECH** — SPEECH is the only correctly spelled word that fits the sentence.
3) **EXPERT** — EXPERT is the only correctly spelled word that fits the sentence.
4) **KITCHEN** — KITCHEN is the only correctly spelled word that fits the sentence.
5) **CASTLE** — CASTLE is the only correctly spelled word that fits the sentence.
6) **AEROPLANE** — AEROPLANE is the only correctly spelled word that fits the sentence.
7) **DAMAGE** — DAMAGE is the only correctly spelled word that fits the sentence.
8) **SPECIES** — SPECIES is the only correctly spelled word that fits the sentence.
9) **PROMISE** — PROMISE is the only correctly spelled word that fits the sentence.
10) **RESERVE** — RESERVE is the only correctly spelled word that fits the sentence.
11) **ANCIENT** — ANCIENT is the only correctly spelled word that fits the sentence.
12) **VICTORY** — VICTORY is the only correctly spelled word that fits the sentence.
13) **PURCHASE** — PURCHASE is the only correctly spelled word that fits the sentence.
14) **PAVEMENT** — PAVEMENT is the only correctly spelled word that fits the sentence.
15) **COMPETE** — COMPETE is the only correctly spelled word that fits the sentence.
16) **BEAUTY** — BEAUTY is the only correctly spelled word that fits the sentence.
17) **PASSION** — PASSION is the only correctly spelled word that fits the sentence.
18) **HEIGHT** — HEIGHT is the only correctly spelled word that fits the sentence.
19) **CLAIMED** — CLAIMED is the only correctly spelled word that fits the sentence.
20) **ESTIMATE** — ESTIMATE is the only correctly spelled word that fits the sentence.

Page 24 — Word Ladders

1) **(HOLD) (HOLE)** — The ladder is: FOLD (HOLD) (HOLE) HOPE
2) **(VEST) (NEST)** — The ladder is: VAST (VEST) (NEST) NEAT
3) **(RICE) (RIDE)** — The ladder is: RICH (RICE) (RIDE) HIDE
4) **(BARN) (BARE)** — The ladder is: BURN (BARN) (BARE) CARE
5) **(BOWS) (TOWS)** — The ladder is: BOWL (BOWS) (TOWS) TOES
6) **(FILE) (PILE)** — The ladder is: FILM (FILE) (PILE) PALE
7) **(NETS) (VETS)** — The ladder is: NEWS (NETS) (VETS) VATS
8) **(BONE) (BOND)** — The ladder is: CONE (BONE) (BOND) BEND
9) **(DEAL) (SEAL)** — The ladder is: DIAL (DEAL) (SEAL) SEAM
10) **(FLAW) (CLAW)** — The ladder is: FLOW (FLAW) (CLAW) CLAD
11) **(HARE) (HIRE)** — The ladder is: HARD (HARE) (HIRE) HIDE
12) **(MEND) (BEND)** — The ladder is: MENU (MEND) (BEND) BAND
13) **(WIDE) (WADE)** — The ladder is: WIFE (WIDE) (WADE) MADE
14) **(YELL) (WELL)** — The ladder is: YELP (YELL) (WELL) WALL
15) **(GAIN) (VAIN)** — The ladder is: GAIT (GAIN) (VAIN) VEIN
16) **(SHOPS) (STOPS)** — The ladder is: SHOES (SHOPS) (STOPS) STEPS
17) **(STORK) (STARK)** — The ladder is: STORM (STORK) (STARK) SHARK
18) **(RIDER) (WIDER)** — The ladder is: RIVER (RIDER) (WIDER) WIDEN
19) **(PEACH) (POACH)** — The ladder is: PEACE (PEACH) (POACH) COACH
20) **(GROVE) (GRAVE)** — The ladder is: DROVE (GROVE) (GRAVE) GRAVY

Section Four — Word Meanings

Page 25 — Closest Meaning

1) **story   tale** — Both of these mean 'narrative'.
2) **attach   fasten** — Both of these mean 'to connect'.
3) **job   occupation** — Both of these mean 'profession'.
4) **stomach   tummy** — Both of these are names for the part of the body where food is digested.
5) **vessel   ship** — Both of these mean 'boat'.
6) **audience   spectators** — Both of these are people who watch an event.
7) **beneath   below** — Both of these mean 'under'.
8) **enquire   ask** — Both of these mean 'to question'.
9) **safety   welfare** — Both of these mean 'wellbeing'.
10) **fragile   delicate** — Both of these mean 'easily damaged'.
11) **chaotic   disorderly** — Both of these mean 'disorganised'.
12) **elevated   raised** — Both of these mean 'high up'.
13) **isolated   secluded** — Both of these mean 'out of the way'.
14) **category   genre** — Both of these mean 'type'.
15) **hidden   concealed** — Both of these mean 'not visible'.
16) **conscious   aware** — Both of these mean 'knowledgeable about something'.
17) **guard   protect** — Both of these mean 'to defend'.
18) **research   investigate** — Both of these mean 'to study'.
19) **prejudice   preconception** — Both of these mean 'a preformed idea'.
20) **blunt   abrupt** — Both of these mean 'short and sudden'.

Page 26 — Closest Meaning

1) **useful** — Both words mean 'beneficial'.
2) **feel** — Both words mean 'to handle'.
3) **sphere** — Both words describe a round, 3D shape.
4) **remain** — Both words mean 'to linger'.
5) **wash** — Both words mean 'to clean with water'.
6) **embed** — Both words mean 'to implant'.
7) **graze** — Both words mean 'scrape'.
8) **terrace** — Both words describe a paved, outdoor area.
9) **chuckle** — Both words mean 'to laugh'.
10) **thump** — Both words mean 'to hit'.
11) **cheerful** — Both words mean 'happy'.
12) **scent** — Both words mean 'smell'.
13) **glimpse** — Both words mean 'to look briefly'.
14) **stray** — Both words mean 'to move away'.
15) **custom** — Both words mean 'tendency'.
16) **criticise** — Both words mean 'to disapprove of'.
17) **humiliate** — Both words mean 'to shame'.
18) **trait** — Both words mean 'characteristic'.
19) **squirm** — Both words mean 'to twist your body'.
20) **fluctuate** — Both words mean 'to change back and forth'.

Page 27 — Closest Meaning

1) **cloth** — Both words mean 'material'.
2) **wail** — Both words mean 'moan'.
3) **attempt** — Both words mean 'to make an effort'.
4) **ground** — Both words describe the surface at the bottom of a room.
5) **rotate** — Both words mean 'to turn'.
6) **tired** — Both words mean 'sleepy'.
7) **organise** — Both words mean 'to put in order'.
8) **border** — Both words mean 'outline'.
9) **hazy** — Both words mean 'difficult to see'.
10) **quiet** — Both words mean 'a lack of noise'.
11) **problem** — Both words mean 'difficulty'.
12) **hazard** — Both words mean 'threat'.
13) **swallow** — Both words mean 'to consume down the throat'.
14) **confident** — Both words mean 'sure of oneself'.
15) **misery** — Both words mean 'unhappiness'.
16) **information** — Both words mean 'facts'.
17) **teach** — Both words mean 'to tutor'.
18) **chart** — Both words describe an accurate drawing of an area of land.
19) **distressed** — Both words mean 'very upset'.
20) **disguise** — Both words mean 'to conceal'.

Page 28 — Opposite Meaning

1) **remember   forget** — 'remember' means 'to recall', whereas 'forget' means 'to fail to recall'.
2) **agile   slow** — 'agile' means 'quick', whereas 'slow' means 'low speed'.
3) **rough   smooth** — 'rough' means 'uneven', whereas 'smooth' means 'even'.
4) **experienced   amateur** — 'experienced' means 'skilled', whereas 'amateur' means 'unskilled'.
5) **thriving   failing** — 'thriving' means 'succeeding', whereas 'failing' means 'not succeeding'.
6) **neglectful   attentive** — 'neglectful' means 'uncaring', whereas 'attentive' means 'caring'.
7) **boisterous   restrained** — 'boisterous' means 'rowdy', whereas 'restrained' means 'reserved'.
8) **stifle   allow** — 'stifle' means 'limit', whereas 'allow' means 'permit'.
9) **indulge   deprive** — 'indulge' means 'to allow something', whereas 'deprive' means 'to deny something'.
10) **affection   dislike** — 'affection' means 'fondness', whereas 'dislike' means 'hostility'.
11) **disperse   accumulate** — 'disperse' means 'to distribute', whereas 'accumulate' means 'to collect'.
12) **divulge   withhold** — 'divulge' means 'to reveal information', whereas 'withhold' means 'to keep back information'.
13) **composed   agitated** — 'composed' means 'calm', whereas 'agitated' means 'flustered'.
14) **forlorn   hopeful** — 'forlorn' means 'lacking hope', whereas 'hopeful' means 'full of hope'.
15) **dubious   believable** — 'dubious' means 'doubtful', whereas 'believable' means 'plausible'.
16) **compassionate   uncaring** — 'compassionate' means 'thoughtful', whereas 'uncaring' means 'not thoughtful'.

17) **vital   inessential** — 'vital' means 'necessary', whereas 'inessential' means 'unnecessary'.

18) **benign   malignant** — 'benign' means 'harmless', whereas 'malignant' means 'harmful'.

19) **submissive   rebellious** — 'submissive' means 'compliant', whereas 'rebellious' means 'defiant'.

20) **harmony   discord** — 'harmony' means 'agreement', whereas 'discord' means 'lack of agreement'.

Page 29 — Opposite Meaning

1) **linger** — 'leave' means 'to go', whereas 'linger' means 'to hang around'.

2) **humble** — 'smug' means 'arrogant', whereas 'humble' means 'modest'.

3) **close** — 'remote' means 'far away', whereas 'close' means 'near'.

4) **inviting** — 'repugnant' means 'off-putting', whereas 'inviting' means 'welcoming'.

5) **bright** — 'gloomy' means 'dark', whereas 'bright' means 'light'.

6) **uncertain** — 'firm' means 'fixed', whereas 'uncertain' means 'likely to change'.

7) **swell** — 'contract' means 'to get smaller', whereas 'swell' means 'to get bigger'.

8) **jovial** — 'miserable' means 'unhappy', whereas 'jovial' means 'happy'.

9) **flamboyant** — 'drab' means 'dull', whereas 'flamboyant' means 'bright and colourful'.

10) **adhere** — 'disobey' means 'to go against', whereas 'adhere' means 'to go along with'.

11) **cynical** — 'trusting' means 'willing to believe others', whereas 'cynical' means 'unwilling to believe others'.

12) **biased** — 'objective' means 'neutral', whereas 'biased' means 'prejudiced'.

13) **contrary** — 'agreeable' means 'easy to get on with', whereas 'contrary' means 'deliberately difficult'.

14) **sincere** — 'devious' means 'dishonest', whereas 'sincere' means 'honest'.

15) **timid** — 'feisty' means 'lively and aggressive', whereas 'timid' means 'shy and fearful'.

16) **anxious** — 'unconcerned' means 'not worried', whereas 'anxious' means 'very worried'.

17) **waive** — 'claim' means 'to state your right to something', whereas 'waive' means 'to give up your right to something'.

18) **inept** — 'adept' means 'competent', whereas 'inept' means 'incompetent'.

19) **capricious** — 'predictable' means 'rarely changing', whereas 'capricious' means 'often changing'.

20) **unequivocal** — 'indefinite' means 'uncertain', whereas 'unequivocal' means 'certain'.

Page 30 — Opposite Meaning

1) **fluid** — 'solid' means 'having a fixed shape', whereas 'fluid' means 'having no fixed shape'.

2) **safe** — 'dangerous' means 'exposed to risk', whereas 'safe' means 'protected from risk'.

3) **minimum** — 'maximum' means 'greatest amount possible', whereas 'minimum' means 'least amount possible'.

4) **ignore** — 'watch' means 'to look', whereas 'ignore' means 'to not look'.

5) **exterior** — 'interior' means 'inside', whereas 'exterior' means 'outside'.

6) **sink** — 'float' means 'to stay on the surface', whereas 'sink' means 'to fall below the surface'.

7) **uncommon** — 'widespread' means 'often seen', whereas 'uncommon' means 'rarely seen'.

8) **different** — 'same' means 'identical', whereas 'different' means 'unalike'.

9) **messy** — 'organised' means 'ordered', whereas 'messy' means 'disordered'.

10) **narrow** — 'broad' means 'wide', whereas 'narrow' means 'not wide'.

11) **sunny** — 'cloudy' means 'darkened by clouds', whereas 'sunny' means 'lit up by the sun'.

12) **descend** — 'climb' means 'to go up', whereas 'descend' means 'to go down'.

13) **fake** — 'authentic' means 'genuine', whereas 'fake' means 'not genuine'.

14) **absent** — 'present' means 'in attendance', whereas 'absent' means 'not in attendance'.

15) **energetic** — 'lazy' means 'lacking energy', whereas 'energetic' means 'full of energy'.

16) **reject** — 'agree' means 'to go along with', whereas 'reject' means 'to go against'.

17) **careless** — 'meticulous' means 'showing attention to detail', whereas 'careless' means 'lacking attention to detail'.

18) **unknown** — 'famous' means 'well-known', whereas 'unknown' means 'not known'.

19) **protected** — 'vulnerable' means 'open to attack', whereas 'protected' means 'shielded from attack'.

20) **erroneous** — 'correct' means 'right', whereas 'erroneous' means 'wrong'.

Page 31 — Multiple Meanings

1) **patient** — 'patient' can mean 'uncomplaining' or 'a person being treated'.

2) **light** — 'light' can mean 'illuminated' or 'weighing little'.

3) **revolt** — 'revolt' can mean 'repel' or 'rebellion'.

4) **edge** — 'edge' can mean 'boundary' or 'upper hand'.

5) **compose** — 'compose' can mean 'to control yourself' or 'to create'.

6) **throw** — 'throw' can mean 'to bewilder' or 'to hurl something'.

7) **dust** — 'dust' can mean 'to remove dirt' or 'to lightly cover with a powder'.

8) **company** — 'company' can mean 'a business' or 'other people'.

9) **overlook** — 'overlook' can mean 'to accidentally ignore' or 'to look down upon'.

10) **crown** — 'crown' can mean 'an accessory worn on the head' or 'the highest point'.

11) **grill** — 'grill' can mean 'to question someone aggressively' or 'to cook food under a grill'.

12) **slack** — 'slack' can mean 'not tight' or 'without proper care'.

13) **buckle** — 'buckle' can mean 'to do up' or 'to crumple'.

14) **atmosphere** — 'atmosphere' can mean 'the mood of a place' or 'the gases around the earth'.

15) **assume** — 'assume' can mean 'to believe without proof' or 'to acquire something'.

16) **mild** — 'mild' can mean 'not extreme in temperature' or 'calm'.

17) **corner** — 'corner' can mean 'the point where two sides meet' or 'to trap in a corner'.

18) **spark** — 'spark' can mean 'to flash' or 'to suddenly start something'.

Page 32 — Odd One Out

1) **student** — The other three are all people who teach others.
2) **congregation** — The other three are all religious buildings.
3) **dry** — The other three are all things found in a desert.
4) **need** — The other three all mean 'to long for'.
5) **fire** — The other three are types of fuel.
6) **ascend** — The other three all mean 'to go downwards'.
7) **rocket** — The other three are not man-made objects.
8) **original** — The other three all mean 'present-day'.
9) **conceal** — The other three all mean 'to encircle'.
10) **release** — The other three all mean 'to take'.
11) **method** — The other three all mean 'an idea'.
12) **surprising** — The other three all mean 'instant'.
13) **revive** — The other three all mean 'to copy'.
14) **incorporate** — The other three mean 'to split apart'.
15) **pensive** — The other three all mean 'bad-tempered'.
16) **answer** — The other three all mean 'to estimate'.
17) **tremble** — The other three all mean 'to fall'.
18) **unwanted** — The other three all mean 'irritating'.
19) **imposing** — The other three all mean 'demanding attention'.
20) **intuitive** — The other three all mean 'imaginative'.

Page 33 — Odd Ones Out

1) **walk   stroll** — The other three all mean 'to move quickly'.
2) **city   town** — The other three are all general terms for a region.
3) **steel   brass** — The other three are types of fabric.
4) **lively   active** — The other three all mean 'fast'.
5) **sundown   dusk** — The other three all describe the beginning of the day.
6) **soil   water** — The other three are parts of a tree.
7) **fix   tools** — The other three are used to fasten things.
8) **money   cash** — The other three are things used instead of money to make a purchase.
9) **roam   wander** — The other three all mean 'to get away from'.
10) **lake   river** — The other three are all names for the land next to a body of water.
11) **adjust   improve** — The other three all mean 'to get bigger'.
12) **appearance   expression** — The other three all mean 'temperament'.
13) **distance   temperature** — The other three are tools used to measure things.
14) **letter   font** — The other three are punctuation marks.

15) **solution   recognition** — The other three all mean 'comprehension'.
16) **overshoot   exceed** — The other three all mean 'to overcome a challenge'.
17) **ministry   government** — The other three all mean 'a rule'.
18) **deplete   diminish** — The other three all mean 'to ruin'.
19) **develop   upgrade** — The other three all mean 'to support'.
20) **notable   obscure** — The other three all mean 'clear'.

Page 34 — Word Connections

1) **rain   sun** — They are what umbrellas and caps protect you from.
2) **sour   sweet** — They are how limes and watermelons taste.
3) **hand   eye** — They are the body parts used to wave and wink.
4) **hoop   goal** — They are the targets to aim for in basketball and football.
5) **flower   soup** — They are what you can put in vases and pans.
6) **ship   plane** — They are the vehicles controlled by sailors and pilots.
7) **sew   dig** — They are the activities performed with needles and trowels.
8) **fly   waddle** — They are how pigeons and penguins move.
9) **insufficient   large** — They are synonyms of 'meagre' and 'considerable'.
10) **assessment   poll** — They are synonyms of 'test' and 'survey'.
11) **slice   pour** — They are what you do with bread and milk.
12) **naughty   polite** — They are synonyms of 'mischievous' and 'courteous'.
13) **buildings   teeth** — They are what architects and dentists work on.
14) **planned   vain** — They are antonyms of 'impulsive' and 'humble'.
15) **stern   forgiving** — They are synonyms of 'strict' and 'lenient'.
16) **dictionary   cookbook** — They are the books in which you can look up words and recipes.
17) **long   question** — They are synonyms of 'hope' and 'doubt'.
18) **accommodation   food** — They are what hotels and supermarkets provide.
19) **flatter   hinder** — They are antonyms of 'offend' and 'assist'.
20) **work   learn** — They are what you do in offices and schools.

Page 35 — Reorder Words To Make A Sentence

1) **with   went** — The sentence is 'Rebecca went to the cinema with some friends'.
2) **up   scurried** — The sentence is 'The squirrel scurried quickly up the tree trunk'.
3) **box   in** — The sentence is 'I discovered an old photograph in that box'.
4) **today   outside** — The sentence is 'It was extremely windy outside the house today'.
5) **local   visit** — The sentence is 'We went to visit some alpacas at the local farm'.
6) **my   a** — The sentence is 'I baked a Victoria sponge cake for my parents'.
7) **travel   fastest** — The sentence is 'The fastest method of transport is to travel by plane'.

8) **We   to** — The sentence is 'To celebrate my friend's birthday, we had a jungle-themed party'.

9) **museum   collection** — The sentence is 'The collection of fossils at the museum is amazing'.

10) **later   camping** — The sentence is 'I am going camping with my family later this year'.

11) **last   started** — The sentence is 'I started to write a fantasy novel last week'.

12) **to   all** — The sentence is 'We built sandcastles all day when we went to the beach'.

13) **Are   our** — The sentence is 'Our favourite flowers are tulips because they are colourful'.

14) **Sheep   the** — The sentence is 'The farmer now has fifty-two sheep in the field'.

15) **on   is** — The sentence is 'Pineapple is my favourite topping to put on pizza'.

16) **pumpkin   bright** — The sentence is 'On Halloween, I dressed up as a bright orange pumpkin'.

17) **delicately   were** — The sentence is 'There were three goldfinches perched delicately on the branch'.

18) **Erupted   a** — The sentence is 'A loud and powerful roar erupted from the lion's mouth'.

19) **found   breathed** — The sentence is 'I breathed a deep sigh of relief when I found my homework down the sofa'.

20) **average   tallest** — The sentence is 'I was the tallest person in my class but now I'm average height'.

Page 36 — Reorder Words To Make A Sentence

Your Child May Have Made A Different Sentence Using The Words Given. This Is Fine, As Long As The Correct Word Has Been Chosen.

1) **it** — The words can be rearranged into the sentence 'The snake slithered slowly across the floor'.

2) **where** — The words can be rearranged into the sentence 'The parrot sat on the pirate's shoulder'.

3) **now** — The words can be rearranged into the sentence 'I played rounders with my friends today'.

4) **evening** — The words can be rearranged into the sentence 'She likes to go stargazing at night'.

5) **seasons** — The words can be rearranged into the sentence 'The leaves turn brown in the autumn'.

6) **age** — The words can be rearranged into the sentence 'My brother is three years older than me'.

7) **wanted** — The words can be rearranged into the sentence 'I would like to own a pet rabbit'.

8) **meal** — The words can be rearranged into the sentence 'He has cereal and a banana for breakfast'.

9) **went** — The words can be rearranged into the sentence 'We are going on holiday to the seaside'.

10) **yesterday** — The words can be rearranged into the sentence 'I really look forward to going to drama club'.

11) **gave** — The words can be rearranged into the sentence 'The teacher looked relieved that my homework was done'.

12) **lots** — The words can be rearranged into the sentence 'We made a fruit salad with oranges and strawberries'.

13) **enjoying** — The words can be rearranged into the sentence 'I respect my friends because they are very kind.'

14) **act** — The words can be rearranged into the sentence 'I am rehearsing every night for our school play'.

15) **eat** — The words can be rearranged into the sentence 'The hungry giraffe found a leaf and chewed it'.

16) **next** — The words can be rearranged into the sentence 'There is a cat that lives on our street'.

17) **because** — The words can be rearranged into the sentence 'I won an award for spelling the most words correctly'.

18) **learnt** — The words can be rearranged into the sentence 'She was determined to perform that song on the violin'.

Section Five — Maths and Sequences

Page 37 — Complete the Sum

1) **6** — $3 \times 6 = 18$, $18 = 24 - 6$
2) **5** — $15 \div 3 = 5$, $5 = 10 - 5$
3) **9** — $8 \times 3 = 24$, $24 = 15 + 9$
4) **9** — $16 \div 4 = 4$, $4 = 13 - 9$
5) **7** — $5 \times 4 - 6 = 14$, $14 = 7 + 7$
6) **5** — $10 \div 2 + 3 = 8$, $8 = 13 - 5$
7) **11** — $7 \times 3 - 4 = 17$, $17 = 6 + 11$
8) **6** — $9 \div 3 + 7 = 10$, $10 = 4 + 6$
9) **3** — $6 \times 4 - 15 = 9$, $9 = 3 \times 3$
10) **5** — $3 \times 6 \div 2 = 9$, $9 = 14 - 5$
11) **5** — $27 \div 3 - 4 = 5$, $5 = 25 \div 5$
12) **5** — $3 \times 8 - 4 = 20$, $20 = 4 \times 5$
13) **2** — $12 \div 3 + 4 = 8$, $8 = 16 \div 2$
14) **8** — $21 \div 3 - 4 = 3$, $3 = 11 - 8$
15) **4** — $4 \times 3 \div 2 = 6$, $6 = 2 + 8 - 4$
16) **2** — $8 \div 2 + 9 - 3 = 10$, $10 = 5 \times 2$
17) **10** — $20 \div 4 \times 8 - 10 = 30$, $30 = 3 \times 10$
18) **6** — $9 \times 2 + 4 = 22$, $22 = 8 \times 2 + 6$
19) **13** — $14 \div 2 \times 3 + 5 = 26$, $26 = 2 \times 13$
20) **6** — $36 \div 6 + 8 - 11 = 3$, $3 = 18 \div 2 - 6$

Page 38 — Letter Sequences

1) **JT** — The first letter moves back 1 letter each time. The second letter moves forward 1 letter each time.

2) **TG** — The first letter moves forward 2 letters each time. The second letter moves back 2 letters each time.

3) **IF** — The first letter moves forward 1 letter then 2 letters alternately. The second letter moves back 4 letters each time.

4) **FA** — Both letters move back 3 letters then 2 letters alternately.

5) **IU** — The first letter moves back 2 letters each time. The second letter moves forward 1 letter then 2 letters alternately.

6) **KH** — The first letter moves forward 3 letters, then the letter repeats once. The second letter moves back 2 letters then 1 letter alternately.

7) **RF** — The first moves back 3 letters each time. The second letter moves forward 1 letter, then the letter repeats once.

8) **IR** — The first letter moves forward 1 letter then back 2 letters alternately. The second letter moves in the sequence -2, -1, 0, +1, +2.

9) **YR** — The first letter moves back 2 letters each time. The second letter moves forward 1 additional letter each time, i.e. +1, +2, +3.

10) **QD** — The first letter moves forward 1 additional letter each time, i.e. +1, +2, +3. The second letter moves forward 2 letters then back 3 letters alternately.

11) **IG** — The first letter moves in the sequence -1, O, +1, +2, +3. The second letter moves back 1 additional letter each time, i.e. -1, -2, -3.

12) **TM** — The first letter moves in the sequence O, -1, -2, -3, -4. The second letter moves forward 3 letters then 6 letters alternately.

13) **LM** — The first letter moves forward 3 letters then back 2 letters alternately. The second letter moves forward 2 letters then back 3 letters alternately.

14) **VI** — The first letter moves in the sequence -1, O, +1, +2, +3. The second letter moves in the sequence -3, -2, -1, O, +1.

15) **PW** — The first letter moves in the sequence +2, +1, O, -1, -2. The second letter moves in the sequence -2, -1, O, +1, +2.

16) **BU** — The first letter moves forward 2 letters then 4 letters alternately. The second letter moves back 2 letters then 1 letter alternately.

17) **MO** — The first letter moves forward 3 letters then back 2 letters alternately. The second letter moves back 1 additional letter each time, i.e. -1, -2, -3.

18) **GJ** — The first letter moves in the sequence +1, O, -1, -2, -3. The second letter moves forward 1 additional letter each time, i.e. +2, +3, +4.

19) **PJ** — The first letter moves forward 3 letters then 1 letter alternately. The second letter moves in the sequence -1, O, +1, +2, +3.

20) **VC** — The first letter moves back 1 additional letter each time, i.e. -1, -2, -3. The second letter moves forward 1 fewer letters each time, I.e. +5, +4, +3, +2.

Page 39 — Number Sequences

1) **16** — Add 3 each time.

2) **5** — Subtract 6 each time.

3) **71** — Add 12 each time.

4) **2** — Halve the number each time.

5) **18** — The number added increases by 1 each time: +1, +2, +3, +4, +5.

6) **49** — These are square numbers, i.e. $2 \times 2 = 4$, $3 \times 3 = 9$, $4 \times 4 = 16$ etc.

7) **16** — There are two sequences which alternate. In the first sequence, the number doubles each time. In the second sequence, the number halves each time.

8) **0** — The number subtracted increases by 1 each time: -1, -2, -3, -4, -5.

9) **9** — The number subtracted doubles each time: -1, -2, -4, -8, -16.

10) **24** — The 2 previous numbers are added together to get the next number in the sequences, i.e. $3 + 3 = 6$, $3 + 6 = 9$ etc.

11) **65** — There are two sequences which alternate. In the first sequence, add 3 each time. In the second sequence, subtract 2 each time.

12) **96** — Add square numbers in ascending order: +4, +9, +16, +25, +36.

13) **11** — There are two sequences which alternate. In the first sequence, add 3 each time. In the second sequence, the number doubles each time.

14) **5** — The numbers follow the sequence +1, O, -1, -2, -3.

15) **8** — The number subtracted doubles each time: -1, -2, -4, -8, -16.

16) **45** — Subtract square numbers in descending order: -25, -16, -9, -4, -1.

17) **29** — Add prime numbers in ascending order: +2, +3, +5, +7, +11.

18) **48** — There are two sequences which alternate. In the first sequence, the number doubles each time. In the second sequence, the number halves each time.

19) **4** — Divide by ascending numbers: ÷2, ÷3, ÷4, ÷5.

20) **27** — There are two sequences which alternate. In both sequences, the number triples each time.

Page 40 — Related Numbers

1) **7** — Add the outer numbers together.

2) **3** — Divide the first number by the third number.

3) **7** — Subtract the third number from the first number.

4) **11** — Find the mid-point between the two outer numbers by adding the outer numbers together and dividing the answer by 2.

5) **8** — Multiply the outer numbers.

6) **9** — Subtract the first number from the third number.

7) **13** — Add the outer numbers together. Subtract 1.

8) **23** — Find the mid-point between the two outer numbers by adding the outer numbers together and dividing the answer by 2.

9) **9** — Divide the third number by the first number.

10) **25** — Multiply the outer numbers. Add 1.

11) **16** — Multiply the outer numbers. Halve the answer.

12) **2** — Subtract the third number from the first number. Halve the answer.

13) **27** — Add 1 to the first number. Multiply the answer by the third number.

14) **9** — Divide the first number by the third number. Multiply the answer by 3.

15) **20** — Multiply the outer numbers. Add 2.

16) **8** — Divide the first number by the third number. Add 1.

17) **12** — Multiply the outer numbers. Divide the answer by 3.

18) **10** — Divide the third number by the first number. Add 3.

19) **28** — Multiply the outer numbers. Subtract 4.

20) **12** — Double the third number. Subtract the first number from the answer.

Page 41 — Letter-Coded Sums

1) **E** — $3 + 5 = 8$, E = 8

2) **D** — $10 - 3 = 7$, D = 7

3) **E** — $2 \times 6 = 12$, E = 12

4) **B** — $8 - 6 + 2 = 4$, B = 4

5) **C** — $3 + 15 - 9 = 9$, C = 9

6) **A** — $3 \times 4 \div 6 = 2$, A = 2

7) **E** — $3 \times 9 - 3 = 24$, E = 24

8) **C** — $28 \div 7 + 4 = 8$, C = 8

9) **C** — $20 - 15 + 4 = 9$, C = 9

10) **E** — $12 \div 3 + 9 = 13$, E = 13

11) **A** — $3 \times 7 \div 21 = 1$, A = 1

12) **C** — $28 \div 4 \times 2 - 2 = 12$, C = 12

13) **E** — $16 \times 2 - 9 + 7 = 30$, E = 30

14) **B** — $6 \times 8 \div 4 - 8 = 4$, B = 4

15) **D** — $32 \div 8 \times 11 - 32 = 12$, D = 12

16) **A** — $3 \times 12 \div 18 + 6 - 5 = 3$, A = 3

Section Six — Logic and Coding

Page 42 — Letter Connections

1) **HI** — Each letter in the pair moves forward 2 letters.

2) **TG** — CX, DW and SH are mirror pairs, where the two letters are an equal distance from the centre of the alphabet. D is 1 letter forward from C, so the missing mirror pair is TG, because T is 1 letter forward from S, and G is its mirror pair.

3) **NM** — Each letter in the pair moves back 4 letters.

4) **YZ** — Each letter in the pair moves forward 10 letters.

5) **PS** — Each letter in the pair moves forward 7 letters.

6) **PR** — Each letter in the pair moves back 6 letters.

7) **AS** — The first letter in the pair moves back 3 letters, the second letter moves forward 5 letters.

8) **MN** — SH, VE and JQ are mirror pairs, where the two letters are an equal distance from the centre of the alphabet. V is 3 letters forward from S, so the missing mirror pair is MN, because M is 3 letters forward from J, and N is its mirror pair.

9) **TP** — Each letter in the pair moves back 5 letters.

10) **HS** — FU, BY and LO are mirror pairs, where the two letters are an equal distance from the centre of the alphabet. B is 4 letters back from F, so the missing pair is HS, because H is 4 letters back from L, and S is its mirror pair.

11) **YN** — The first letter in the pair moves forward 10 letters, the second letter moves back 6 letters.

12) **GT** — PK, UF and BY are mirror pairs, where the two letters are an equal distance from the centre of the alphabet. U is 5 letters forward from P, so the missing pair is GT, because G is 5 letters forward from B, and T is its mirror pair.

13) **WS** — The first letter in the pair moves back 9 letters, the second letter moves forward 3 letters.

14) **ZX** — JQ and LO are mirror pairs, where the two letters are an equal distance from the centre of the alphabet. The answer will be the mirror pairs for A and C, which are Z and X.

15) **PZ** — The first letter in the pair moves forward 3 letters, the second letter moves back 6 letters.

16) **BS** — IR and NM are mirror pairs, where the two letters are an equal distance from the centre of the alphabet. The answer will be the mirror pairs for Y and H, which are B and S.

17) **OL** — ZA, SH and VE are mirror pairs, where the two letters are an equal distance from the centre of the alphabet. S is 7 letters back from Z, so the missing pair is OL, because O is 7 letters back from V, and L is its mirror pair.

18) **QF** — The first letter in the pair moves forward 11 letters, the second letter moves back 6 letters.

19) **NV** — TG and WD are mirror pairs, where the two letters are an equal distance from the centre of the alphabet. The answer will be the mirror pairs for E and M, which are V and N, but the letters are reversed.

20) **KQ** — UF and BY are mirror pairs, where the two letters are an equal distance from the centre of the alphabet. The answer will be the mirror pairs for J and P, which are Q and K, but the letters are reversed.

Page 43 — Letter-Word Codes

1) **UWP** — To get from the word to the code move each letter forward 2.

2) **BAN** — This is a mirror code, where each letter is an equal distance from the centre of the alphabet. Y is 12 letters forward from the centre, and B is 12 letters back; Z is 13 letters forward, and A is 13 letters back; and M is 1 letter back, and N is 1 letter forward.

3) **HORN** — To get from the code to the word move each letter forward 3.

4) **RATE** — This is a mirror code, where each letter is an equal distance from the centre of the alphabet. I is 5 letters back from the centre, and R is 5 letters forward; Z is 13 letters forward, and A is 13 letters back; G is 7 letters back, and T is 7 letters forward; and V is 9 letters forward and E is 9 letters back.

5) **UGJR** — To get from the word to the code move the letters in the sequence +1, -1, +1, -1.

6) **WIND** — To get from the code to the word move the letters in the sequence +2, -1, +2, -1.

7) **INDEX** — This is a mirror code, where each letter is an equal distance from the centre of the alphabet. R is 5 letters forward from the centre, and I is 5 letters back; M is 1 letter back, and N is 1 letter forward; W is 10 letters forward, and D is 10 letters back; V is 9 letters forward, and E is 9 letters back; and C is 11 letters back, and X is 11 letters forward.

8) **FXEN** — To get from the word to the code move the letters in the sequence +2, +3, +2, +3.

9) **GIANT** — This is a mirror code, where each letter is an equal distance from the centre of the alphabet. T is 7 letters forward from the centre, and G is 7 letters back; R is 5 letters forward, and I is 5 letters back; Z is 13 letters forward, and A is 13 letters back; M is 1 letter back, and N is 1 letter forward; and G is 7 letters back, and T is 7 letters forward.

10) **HAM** — To get from the code to the word move the letters in the sequence -1, -2, -3.

11) **FUDGE** — This is a mirror code, where each letter is an equal distance from the centre of the alphabet. U is 8 letters forward from the centre, and F is 8 letters back; F is 8 letters back, and U is 8 letters forward; W is 10 letters forward, and D is 10 letters back; T is 7 letters forward, and G is 7 letters back; and V is 9 letters forward, and E is 9 letters back.

12) **BRING** — To get from the code to the word move the letters in the sequence 0, +1, +2, +3, +4.

13) **NLCRZ** — To get from the word to the code move the letters in the sequence -2, 0, +2, +4, +6.

14) **BEANS** — This is a mirror code, where each letter is an equal distance from the centre of the alphabet. Y is 12 letters forward from the centre, and B is 12 letters back; V is 9 letters forward, and E is 9 letters back; Z is 13 letters forward, and A is 13 letters back; M is 1 letter back, and N is 1 letter forward; and H is 6 letters back, and S is 6 letters forward.

15) **ROUND** — To get from the code to the word move the letters in the sequence +2, +1, 0, -1, -2.

Pages 44-45 — Number-Word Codes

1) **5624** — L = 5, O = 6, U = 2, D = 4
2) **1654** — H = 1, O = 6, L = 5, D = 4
3) **LUSH** — L = 5, U = 2, S = 3, H = 1
4) **2651** — P = 2, L = 6, A = 5, Y = 1
5) **3461** — R = 3, E = 4, L = 6, Y = 1
6) **YEAR** — Y = 1, E = 4, A = 5, R = 3
7) **1546** — B = 1, E = 5, N = 4, D = 6
8) **3556** — H = 3, E = 5, E = 5, D = 6
9) **HIND** — H = 3, I = 2, N = 4, D = 6
10) **4352** — T = 4, O = 3, A = 5, D = 2
11) **1362** — W = 1, O = 3, R = 6, D = 2
12) **ROAD** — R = 6, O = 3, A = 5, D = 2
13) **5321** — C = 5, O = 3, M = 2, A = 1
14) **2314** — M = 2, O = 3, A = 1, T = 4
15) **TACO** — T = 4, A = 1, C = 5, O = 3
16) **1454** — M = 1, E = 4, R = 5, E = 4
17) **2451** — T = 2, E = 4, R = 5, M = 1
18) **TRUE** — T = 2, R = 5, U = 3, E = 4
19) **2415** — O = 2, N = 4, C = 1, E = 5
20) **1265** — C = 1, O = 2, D = 6, E = 5
21) **ENDS** — E = 5, N = 4, D = 6, S = 3
22) **6123** — R = 6, A = 1, G = 2, E = 3
23) **6354** — R = 6, E = 3, N = 5, D = 4
24) **GEAR** — G = 2, E = 3, A = 1, R = 6

Page 46 — Word Grids

1) 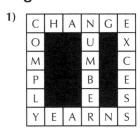   2)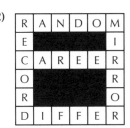

This is the only way all the words fit together in the grid.

3)    4)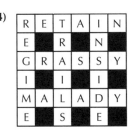

This is the only way all the words fit together in the grid.

5)    6)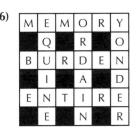

This is the only way all the words fit together in the grid.

7) 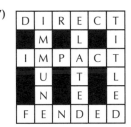   8)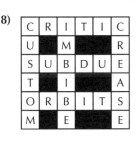

This is the only way all the words fit together in the grid.

9)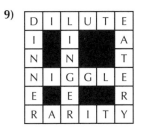

This is the only way all the words fit together in the grid.

Section Seven — Completing Passages

Page 47 — Using Rules of English

1) **want** — The sentence should be 'I **want** to paint my room yellow because I love bright colours.'
2) **get** — The sentence should be 'My dad asks me to do my homework as soon as I **get** in from school.'
3) **since** — The sentence should be 'Oliver has been learning to swim **since** he was three years old.'
4) **though** — The sentence should be 'We wanted to go to the circus even **though** it was raining.'
5) **like** — The sentence should be 'I **like** visiting my grandparents at the weekend.'
6) **made** — The sentence should be 'Ava had **made** a friendship bracelet for Emily.'
7) **either** — The sentence should be 'They are going to watch a film on **either** Friday or Saturday.'
8) **but** — The sentence should be 'We tried to make flapjacks last night, **but** we forgot to add the syrup.'
9) **saw** — The sentence should be 'I **saw** an old-fashioned steam train with my brother today.'
10) **only** — The sentence should be 'It is **only** six weeks until the summer holidays begin.'
11) **waved** — The sentence should be 'I **waved** happily at the postman as he walked past.'
12) **I** — The sentence should be 'Rosie and **I** have been friends since we were five.'
13) **show** — The sentence should be 'Sibi will **show** us his card tricks at lunchtime tomorrow.'
14) **reclined** — The sentence should be 'When Freya **reclined** on the sofa, she started to fall asleep.'
15) **joyfully** — The sentence should be 'The sheep bounced **joyfully** across the field.'
16) **scored** — The sentence should be 'Amir **scored** three goals during the football match yesterday.'
17) **could** — The sentence should be 'Leila **could** smell the pizza whilst it cooked in the oven.'
18) **did** — The sentence should be 'I **did** my best on the spelling test earlier this week.'

124

Pages 48-49 — Choose a Word

1) **means** — 'which **means** they usually appear at night'
2) **unlike** — 'What makes them **unlike** other species'
3) **their** — 'is **their** distinctive heart-shaped faces'
4) **are** — 'They **are** found on'
5) **continent** — 'every **continent** in the world'
6) **search** — 'I **search** for the rarest shell'
7) **can** — 'rarest shell I **can** find'
8) **discovering** — 'best chance of **discovering** a new shell'
9) **soon** — 'as **soon** as possible after high tide'
10) **before** — '**before** anyone else has had time to comb'
11) **extended** — 'Hadrian's Wall **extended** for 73 miles'
12) **took** — 'the wall **took** around six years to build'
13) **and** — '**and** was up to six metres high'
14) **embedded** — 'There were forts **embedded** into the wall'
15) **housed** — 'which **housed** hundreds of soldiers at a time'
16) **went** — 'I **went** to a tropical butterfly house'
17) **with** — '**with** my friend Ahmad'
18) **enjoy** — 'he used to **enjoy** going with his family'
19) **favourite** — 'would sketch his **favourite** species in a notebook'
20) **magnificent** — 'We saw a **magnificent** array of butterflies'
21) **opinion** — 'in my **opinion**'
22) **near** — 'Located **near** the northeastern coast'
23) **of** — 'northeastern coast **of** Australia'
24) **resembles** — 'Although it **resembles** a plant'
25) **benefits** — 'One of the many **benefits** of coral reef ecosystems'
26) **includes** — '**includes** their ability to protect shores from storms'
27) **threatened** — 'This is something that is **threatened** by the rising temperatures'

Pages 50-51 — Fill in Missing Letters

1) co**r**ner — 'Standing elegantly in the **corner**'
2) Grow**ing** — '**Growing** up, we would wander'
3) bott**om** — 'to the **bottom** of the garden'
4) deli**ci**ous — 'My grandma would then bake a **delicious** apple crumble'
5) eager**ly** — 'me and my brother **eagerly** awaiting'
6) nosta**l**gic — 'I still get **nostalgic**'
7) waft**ing** — '**wafting** from the oven'
8) temperatures — 'global **temperatures** were significantly colder'
9) toda**y** — 'than they are **today**'
10) froze — 'the River Thames, in London, completely **froze**'
11) ingenui**ty** — 'in an act of **ingenuity**'
12) diverse — 'A **diverse** range of sights could be seen'
13) football — 'from food stalls to **football** pitches'
14) extraordinary — 'an **extraordinary** sight to behold'
15) nig**ht** — 'in the sky at **night**'
16) resu**lt** — 'as a **result** of numerous asteroids and meteorites'
17) surf**ace** — 'colliding with its **surface**'
18) critical — 'plays a **critical** role in controlling Earth's ocean tides'
19) stepp**ed** — 'twelve people have **stepped** foot on the Moon since 1969'
20) explo**r**ations — 'However, **explorations** and research are ongoing'

21) de**t**ermine — 'to **determine** whether life exists there'
22) inte**re**st — 'an **interest** in machinery'
23) com**p**uter — 'the founder of **computer** programming'
24) befriended — 'Lovelace later **befriended** a fellow mathematician'
25) machines — 'that **machines** could be used'
26) comple**x** — 'to perform **complex** mathematical functions'
27) October — 'commemorated on Lovelace Day, every **October**'
28) scientific — 'other influential **scientific** achievements'
29) landed — 'Snowflakes **landed** gently on Lola's smiling face'
30) beneath — 'The ground **beneath** her'
31) sense — 'an overwhelming **sense** of admiration'
32) mornin**g** — 'for this beautiful winter **morning**'
33) glis**t**ening — 'The **glistening** landscape'
34) undis**t**ur**b**ed — 'was so **undisturbed**'
35) relishing — '**relishing** the sound of the muffled crunch below'
36) northern — 'Situated in **northern** India'
37) enorm**ous** — 'in an **enormous** garden'
38) memo**r**y — 'commissioned in **memory** of the Emperor's late wife'
39) decorated — 'is **decorated** with a variety of semi-precious stones'
40) impressive — 'Reaching an **impressive** height'
41) features — 'it **features** an awe-inspiring central dome'
42) recogn**i**sed — 'of this universally **recognised** building'

Section Eight — Comprehension

Pages 52-53 — Finding Hidden Facts

1) **Aisha** — Aisha has seen five animals: a squirrel, a bee, a hedgehog, a butterfly and a sparrow.
2) **Amber** — Amber only plays one instrument: the guitar.
3) **Oscar** — Oscar uses four colours: orange, blue, pink and green.
4) **Ben** — Ben only has one belonging in his rucksack: a bottle.
5) **Rupy** — Rupy only saw two farm animals: a duck and a chicken.
6) **Poppy** — Poppy only has two classes: French and English.
7) **Annette** — Annette is having three types of vegetable: carrots, broccoli and courgette.
8) **Rupert** — Rupert bakes four types of cake: victoria sponge, carrot cake, lemon drizzle and chocolate cake.

Pages 54-55 — Solve the Riddle

1) **D** — Kai picked four apples. Olga picked one fewer apple than Kai and two fewer than Eve, so Olga picked three apples and Eve picked five apples. Dev didn't pick the most apples, and Charlie picked fewer than Dev, so Eve must have picked the most apples.
2) **A** — Ava is thinking of a number lower than 3. Because Nick is the only one thinking of the number 1, Ava must be thinking of the number 2. Saira is thinking of a number twice as big as Ava, so she must be thinking of the number 4.
3) **B** — Ria's birthday is on Saturday. Louise's birthday is two days before Harriet's, so it cannot be on Saturday or Sunday. Therefore, Ria and Louise cannot have the same birthday.

Answers

4) **D** — Jake is 2 cm taller than Dan, who is 125 cm tall, so Jake is 127 cm tall. Viv is 3 cm shorter than Jake, so she must be 124 cm tall. Becky is taller than Dan, so she must be taller than 125 cm. The shortest height is 120 cm, so Maria must be 120 cm tall.

5) **E** — Joe threw the javelin twice as far as the shortest throw, and Simon threw it further, so neither of them had the shortest throw. Ernie's was also not the shortest throw, and Rita threw the furthest, so Rose must have had the shortest throw. Therefore, Ernie could not have thrown the javelin the same distance as Rose.

6) **C** — It is 6.3° C where Mo lives and 5° C where Rob lives. The highest temperature is 2.6° C higher than the second highest. It's only 1.3° C difference between where Mo and Rob live, and Orla lives somewhere colder than Mo, so the highest temperature must be 2.6° C higher than 6.3° C. This means the highest temperature is 8.9° C and the second highest is 6.3° C, so Rob cannot live in the second warmest place.

Page 56 — Understanding the Language in the Text

1) **C** — The fact that Sam sighs suggests that he isn't concerned by the strange noise and would rather go back to sleep.

2) **A** — The comparison tells you that the light is bright because floodlights are very bright.

3) **B** — Grace is being ironic — the sheep is "small" and not very scary at all.

4) **A** — The image of an explorer makes Grace sound brave because explorers go to places people haven't been before.

5) **B** — The adjective "inky" describes something that is black, so this tell you that it is very dark in the tent.

6) **C** — By describing the animal as "two eyes", the author creates tension because the reader doesn't know what the animal is and whether Grace should be afraid of it.

Page 57 — Understanding the Language in the Text

1) **A** — The word "distinctive" means 'easy to spot', so this means the phone boxes are easily recognisable.

2) **B** — In the passage, it says that the original red phone boxes were "too large" to be used across the country, so the cast-iron phone boxes became popular because they weighed a quarter of a tonne less.

3) **C** — There were more than 20 000 phone boxes in the UK "by the turn of the decade". The decade being referred to is the 1930s, so the turn of the decade is the start of 1940.

4) **A** — According to the passage, "most people now carry their own phone", so people don't need to use phone boxes as often.

5) **B** — The phrase "new lease of life" means that the old phone boxes are now being used in new ways.

6) **B** — The word "innovative" means that the communities are being creative in finding new ways to use their phone boxes.

Pages 58-60 — Mixed Comprehension Questions

1) **C** — The girls ran "helter-skelter" through the passages which means that they ran quickly and from side to side.

2) **C** — Riddles are difficult to solve, so by comparing a schoolgirl's mind to a riddle, the author suggests that it's sometimes difficult to know what schoolgirls are thinking.

3) **B** — The fact that Miss Birks lets the girls explore the school grounds is not mentioned in the text as a reason why the girls like her. Instead, the passage mentions that Mrs Trevellyan gives the girls permission to use the grounds.

4) **C** — In the passage it says that nowhere else in Britain "could in any way compare" to the location of the Dower House, which means the girls can't imagine a better location.

5) **D** — In the passage it says that she ruled "with a hand so light that few realised its firmness" which means that she is in charge but doesn't show off her authority.

6) **A** — In the passage it says that the girls only behaved like this "on the first night of a new term", so the author doesn't want the reader to think they usually act this way.

7) **B** — The comparison of the peninsula to a "convent garden" shows that the girls are protected from danger because convents are "safe and secluded" places.

8) **A** — "attributes" means 'characteristics'. Both words refer to the qualities of a thing or person.

9) **B** — "liberty" means 'freedom'. The girls have one night of freedom before the start of the school term.

10) **C** — "transgressed" means 'disobeyed'. The girls rarely disobey Miss Birks's rules.

Assessment Tests

Pages 61-66 — Assessment Test 1

1) **A** — The Gnome travels with Ned and shows him where to find the fairies, so he is helpful.

2) **D** — The Gnome points out the Fairy of the Lake to Ned as she walks "over the bridge" which hangs above a "miniature Niagara".

3) **C** — In the passage it says that the potion will allow Ned to return to his "natural shape".

4) **C** — In the passage it says that the fairies were moving in the grass "like the flowers they represented".

5) **D** — The Gnome guesses that the Fairy of the Lake is crossing the bridge to brew a potion, but says "I dare say", which suggests that he does not know for certain.

6) **C** — In the passage it says that Ned follows the Fairy of the Lake, "not heeding" the Gnome and "almost treading" on fairies, which suggests he is so impatient to speak to her that he notices nothing else.

7) **C** — "stooped" means 'bent down', so Ned is bending down to look through the door because he is much bigger than it.

8) **B** — A 'thimble' is a small cover shaped like a cup, so a "thimbleful" is 'a small amount'.

9) **A** — "exquisite" means 'beautiful and delicate'. The fairies make the palace look beautiful with their decorations.

10) **A** — "distorted" is closest in meaning to 'misshapen'.

11) **DEN** — The complete word is SUDDEN.

12) **KIN** — The complete word is WALKING.

13) **THE** — The complete word is WEATHER.

14) **AGE** — The complete word is BAGEL.

15) **OIL** — The complete word is BOILING.

16) **GET** — The complete word is FORGETS.

17) **PAN** — The complete word is EXPAND.

18) **COW** — The complete word is SCOWLED.

19) **eat** — Rearrange letters 1, 2, 3 in the order 2, 3, 1.

20) **nap** — Rearrange letters 1, 3, 4 in the order 4, 3, 1.

21) **rake** — Rearrange letters 2, 3, 4, 5 in the order 5, 2, 3, 4.

22) **drip** — Rearrange letters 1, 2, 3, 4 in the order 4, 2, 3, 1.

23) **dare** — Rearrange letters 2, 3, 4, 5 in the order 4, 3, 2, 5.

24) **tore** — Rearrange letters 1, 2, 4, 6 in the order 6, 4, 1, 2.

25) **PC** — The first letter in the pair moves forward 2 letters each time. The second letter moves back 3 letters each time.

26) **YD** — The first letter in the pair moves forward 2 letters each time. The second letter moves forward 5 letters each time.

27) **FH** — The first letter in the pair moves back 2 letters each time. The second letter moves back 4 letters each time.

28) **RW** — The first letter in the pair moves forward 1 letter each time. The second letter moves forward 2 letters, then back 1 letter alternately.

29) **SA** — The first letter in the pair moves back 2 letters, then forward 1 letter alternately. The second letter moves forward 3 letters each time.

30) **PY** — The first letter in the pair moves forward 2 letters then 3 letters alternately. The second letter in the pair moves back 2 letters then 1 letter alternately.

31) **JB** — The first letter in the pair moves forward 5 letters then back 3 letters alternately. The second letter moves forward one additional letter each time: +1, +2, +3, +4, +5.

32) **JU** — The first letter in the pair moves back one additional letter each time: -1, -2, -3, -4, -5. The second letter moves in the sequence -1, -2, -1, -2, -1.

33) **land** — 'land' can mean 'an area of ground' or 'to arrive on the ground'.

34) **punch** — 'punch' can mean 'to make a hole in something' or 'to hit with your fist'.

35) **play** — 'play' can mean 'to perform a part' or 'to take part in'.

36) **construct** — 'construct' can mean 'to build something' or 'something created by the mind'.

37) **drill** — 'drill' can mean 'to use a tool to make a hole' or 'a training activity'.

38) **quarters** — 'quarters' can mean 'four equal parts' or 'a place where someone lives'.

39) **fairly** — 'fairly' can mean 'quite' or 'in the right way'.

40) **4** — 19 + 9 = 4 × 7

41) **3** — 12 + 3 = 5 × 3

42) **24** — 16 − 8 = 24 ÷ 3

43) **8** — 34 ÷ 2 = 9 + 8

44) **FUEL** — To get from the code to the word move each letter back 2.

45) **LIFE** — To get from the code to the word move each letter forward 1.

46) **CRQH** — To get from the word to the code move each letter forward 3.

47) **QFZE** — To get from the word to the code move the letters in the sequence -1, +1, -1, +1.

48) **GRIN** — This is a mirror code, where each letter is an equal distance from the centre of the alphabet. T is 7 letters forward, and G is 7 letters back; I is 5 letters back, and R is 5 letters forward; R is 5 letters forward, and I is 5 letters back; and M is 1 letter back and N is 1 letter forward.

49) **QCJI** — To get from the word to the code move each letter in the sequence +1, +2, +3, +4.

50) **JUMP** — This is a mirror code, where each letter is an equal distance from the centre of the alphabet. Q is 4 letters forward, and J is 4 letters back; F is 8 letters back, and U is 8 letters forward; N is 1 letter forward and M is 1 letter back; K is 3 letters back and P is 3 letters forward.

51) **WAKE** — To get from the code to the word move the letters in the sequence: -2, +1, -2, +1.

52) **chicken goose** — The other three are all four-legged animals.

53) **aubergine pumpkin** — The other three are all green vegetables.

54) **armadillo platypus** — The other three are all mythical creatures.

55) **artwork portrait** — The other three are all tools used by an artist.

56) **song music** — The other three are all genres of music.

57) **drawbridge moat** — The other three are all large buildings.

58) **owner voter** — The other three all mean 'a person who lives in a place'.

59) **diligent compulsive** — The other three all mean 'boring'.

60) **difficulty protractor** — The other three are mathematical problems to be solved.

61) **cycling swimming** — The other three are all ball games.

62) **infectious ghostly** — The other three all mean 'glum'.

63) **severe** — Both words mean 'tough'.

64) **renowned** — Both words mean 'well-known'.

65) **whole** — Both words mean 'complete'.

66) **banquet** — Both words mean 'a large meal for many people'.

67) **ordinary** — Both words mean 'usual'.

68) **reasonable** — Both words mean 'rational'.

69) **persistent** — Both words mean 'willing to persevere'.

70) **colossal** — Both words mean 'enormous'.

71) **emerge** — Both words mean 'to come into view'.

72) **tendency** — Both words mean 'a leaning towards a particular way of doing things'.

73) **Maisie** — Maisie buys four items: a key ring, a postcard, a pen and a bookmark.

74) **Luke** — Luke takes part in two events: the sack race and the relay.

Pages 67-72 — Assessment Test 2

1) **B** — In the passage it says that "Arthur Lockwood was working late" and then describes him as the Prime Minister, "engrossed in his work".

2) **D** — In the passage it says that "Street lamps glowed" on London's streets.

3) **D** — The weather is not mentioned in the text.

4) **B** — The private secretary makes a "stifled yawn", which suggests that he is tired.

5) **A** — The envelope is "sealed", which the Prime Minister thinks is "odd".

6) **B** — The grandfather clock has marked time "for every British Prime Minister since Gladstone".

7) **C** — The private secretary is in "an adjoining room", which means 'a room next to another room'.

8) **A** — "churning out" means 'producing lots of something at great speed'.

9) **D** — "engrossed in" is closest in meaning to 'absorbed in'.

10) **B** — "Methodically" is closest in meaning to 'systematically'.

11) **dump** — 'dump' can mean 'to get rid of' or 'a dirty and untidy place'.

12) **chest** — 'chest' can mean 'a large box' or 'the upper part of the body'.

13) **grounds** — 'grounds' can mean 'the area of land surrounding a building' or 'the basis for a decision'.

14) **drive** — 'drive' can mean 'the will to do something' or 'an outing in a vehicle'.

15) **joint** — 'joint' can mean 'used by two people' or 'the point at which two things meet'.

16) **patch** — 'patch' can mean 'a piece of land' or 'to repair'.

17) **model** — 'model' can mean 'a replica' or 'exemplary'.

18) **established** — 'established' can mean 'in a solid position' or 'set up'.

19) **obscure** — 'obscure' can mean 'little-known' or 'to cover'.

20) **design** — 'design' can mean 'a drawing' or 'a plan with a purpose'.

21) **pillar   column** — Both words mean 'a vertical support for a building'.

22) **mob   gang** — Both words mean 'a group of people'.

23) **panel   board** — Both words mean 'a length of wood'.

24) **chapter   section** — Both words mean 'part of a book'.

25) **expand   grow** — Both words mean 'to get bigger'.

26) **OX** — The first letter in the pair moves forward 2 letters each time. The second letter moves forward 3 letters each time.

27) **AS** — The first letter in the pair moves back 2 letters each time. The second letter moves back 3 letters each time.

28) **SE** — The first letter in the pair moves forward one additional letter each time: +1, +2, +3, +4, +5. The second letter moves back 2 letters each time.

29) **EA** — The first letter in the pair moves forward 2 letters, then back 1 letter alternately. The second letter moves back 2 letters each time.

30) **DZ** — The first letter in the pair moves forward 2 letters then 1 letter alternately. The second letter moves back 2 letters then 1 letter alternately.

31) **CL** — The first letter in the pair moves in the sequence 0, +1, +2, +3, +4. The second letter moves in the sequence 0, -1, -2, -3, -4.

32) **treadmill** — 'treadmill' is the only correctly spelled word that can be made.

33) **shipyard** — 'shipyard' is the only correctly spelled word that can be made.

34) **downside** — 'downside' is the only correctly spelled word that can be made.

35) **newborn** — 'newborn' is the only correctly spelled word that can be made.

36) **eyesore** — 'eyesore' is the only correctly spelled word that can be made.

37) **snippet** — 'snippet' is the only correctly spelled word that can be made.

38) **always eats** — The hidden word is 'seat'.

39) **was hefty** — The hidden word is 'wash'.

40) **first opportunity** — The hidden word is 'stop'.

41) **over before** — The hidden word is 'verb'.

42) **broken umbrella** — The hidden word is 'numb'.

43) **helped get** — The hidden word is 'edge'.

44) **di**ved — 'Charlie **dived** into the water'

45) sur**fac**e — 'As he broke the **surface** of the pool'

46) **clamped** — 'he **clamped** his mouth shut'

47) **chee**ring — 'the buzz of **cheering** spectators'

48) muf**fled** — 'the sounds were now **muffled**'

49) **Suddenly** — '**Suddenly**, his head shot up through the water'

50) sp**lashing** — 'the frantic sounds of **splashing** and shouting'

51) **breath** — 'he twisted his head and took a deep **breath**.'

52) for**ward** — 'propelling him **forward** through the clear water.'

53) **rhythm** — 'Just as he was settling into a **rhythm**'

54) tur**ned** — 'he tumbled and **turned**'

55) thoug**ht**s — 'his **thoughts** turned to the other swimmers'

56) glim**pses** — 'he caught **glimpses** of them'

57) **vision** — 'moving in and out of his **vision**'

58) **certainly** — 'It was **certainly** going to be a close finish'

59) **fat** — Take letter 3 from the first word, followed by letter 2 from the second word and then letter 4 from the first word.

60) **elf** — Take letters 4 and 2 from the first word, followed by letter 1 from the second word.

61) **bun** — Take letters 4 and 3 from the first word, followed by letter 1 from the second word.

62) **pat** — Take letter 3 from the second word, followed by letter 4 from the first word and then letter 1 from the second word.

63) **wed** — Take letter 3 from the second word, followed by letter 2 from the first word and then letter 1 from the second word.

64) **rent** — Take letter 3 from the first word, followed by letters 4 and 2 from the second word and then letter 4 from the first word.

65) **pleasant** — 'awful' means 'very bad', whereas 'pleasant' means 'good'.

66) **calm** — 'wild' means 'chaotic', whereas 'calm' means 'tranquil'.

67) **conclude** — 'begin' means 'to start', whereas 'conclude' means 'to end'.

68) **suitable** — 'unfit' means 'not appropriate', whereas 'suitable' means 'appropriate'.

69) **foolish** — 'wise' means 'sensible or well-judged', whereas 'foolish' means 'stupid or poorly judged'.

70) **extract** — 'inject' means 'to put something in', whereas 'extract' means 'to take something out'.

71) **repulse** — 'tempt' means 'to attract', whereas 'repulse' means 'to repel'.

72) **straighten** — 'distort' means 'to twist out of shape', whereas 'straighten' means 'to put back in shape'.

73) **D** — If Tim ran the same distance as Charlotte, and Charlotte ran further than Beth, then Tim also ran further than Beth. Beth ran 10 km, so Tim must have run further than 10 km.

74) **C** — Everyone has at least one cousin, so Isla must have at least one cousin. Isla has the fewest number of cousins, so Amanda must have at least two cousins. Sven has twice as many cousins as Amanda, so Sven must have at least four cousins. Yusuf has exactly four cousins, so he cannot have more cousins than Sven.

Pages 73-78 — Assessment Test 3

1) **B** — The writer closes their eyes to escape from the "truth" that Kamilo Beach is covered in "plastic debris".

2) **C** — In the passage it says that while "change relies heavily" on governments, people can still "individually make a difference".

3) **A** — The writer is "cautiously optimistic" that one day the world's beaches will be plastic-free.

4) **B** — In the passage it says that plastic "can prove fatal to marine animals".

5) **D** — In the passage, there is no mention of how long it takes for microplastics to form.

6) **C** — The writer says the name "Plastic Beach" is "unsettling", which suggests they feel troubled by it.

7) **A** — The writer suggests "cutting down" on single-use plastics, but doesn't suggest banning them completely.

8) **A** — "pristine" is closest in meaning to 'untouched'.

9) **D** — "infinite" is closest in meaning to 'limitless'.

10) **B** — The phrase 'to be a magnet' means 'to attract', so this means that a lot of plastic that is floating in the ocean ends up on Kamilo Beach.

11) **21** — Add the two outer numbers together.

12) **48** — Multiply the outer numbers.

13) **19** — Multiply the outer numbers. Add 5.

14) **9** — Subtract the first number from the third number. Divide the answer by 2.

15) **42** — Add 1 to the first number. Multiply the answer by the third number.

16) **10** — Divide the first number by the third number. Double the answer.

17) **A** — 4 + 13 – 14 = 3, A = 3

18) **D** — 3 × 2 + 5 = 11, D = 11

19) **B** — 24 ÷ 3 – 4 = 4, B = 4

20) **E** — 7 × 4 ÷ 2 = 14, E = 14

21) **B** — 22 + 8 – 16 – 6 = 8, B = 8

22) **B** — 21 ÷ 3 + 2 – 6 = 3, B = 3

23) **t** — The new words are 'flat', 'told', 'feet' and 'tear'.

24) **l** — The new words are 'rail', 'land', 'coil' and 'life'.

25) **m** — The new words are 'swam', 'male', 'sum' and 'mess'.

26) **w** — The new words are 'blew', 'wilt', 'thaw' and 'wood'.

27) **k** — The new words are 'tank', 'keen', 'peak' and 'kind'.

28) **d** — The new words are 'fled', 'damp', 'maid' and 'dove'.

29) **p** — The new words are 'leap', 'pose', 'seep' and 'plot'.

30) **pencil   paper** — The other three are all types of hand-written messages.

31) **reliable   dependable** — The other three mean 'not fake'.

32) **grate   chop** — The other three are all words that describe how food tastes.

33) **describe   illustrate** — The other three mean 'to visualise'.

34) **drive   perform** — They are what chauffeurs and actors do.

35) **playground   cinema** — They are the places where seesaws and popcorn are often found.

36) **big   small** — They are synonyms of 'mammoth' and 'puny'.

37) **length   time** — They are what centimetres and hours measure.

38) **solid   empty** — They are antonyms of 'hollow' and 'occupied'.

39) **reptile   mammal** — They are the classes that each animal belongs to.

40) **restless** — Both words mean 'unsettled'.

41) **deter** — Both words mean 'to persuade against'.

42) **aspire** — Both words mean 'to target'.

43) **dismayed** — Both words mean 'sad'.

44) **endanger** — Both words mean 'to put at risk'.

45) **reliance** — Both words mean 'a need for something or someone'.

46) **charity** — Both words mean 'kindness'.

47) **ensure** — Both words mean 'to make certain'.

48) **surged** — Both words mean 'flowed quickly'.

49) **embraced** — Both words mean 'held close'.

50) **intact** — Both words mean 'not damaged'.

51) **banish** — Both words mean 'to expel'.

52) **t** — The new words are 'tile' and 'them'.

53) **r** — The new words are 'dive' and 'port'.

54) **o** — The new words are 'fund' and 'soon'.

55) **l** — The new words are 'fair' and 'rule'.

56) **h** — The new words are 'tank' and 'hair'.

57) **u** — The new words are 'debt' and 'unit'.

58) **ride** — Rearrange letters 2, 3, 4, 5 in the order 5, 2, 3, 4.

59) **beat** — Rearrange letters 2, 3, 4, 5 in the order 3, 2, 4, 5.

60) **tray** — Rearrange letters 2, 4, 5, 6 in the order 5, 2, 4, 6.

61) **maps** — Rearrange letters 1, 2, 3, 4 in the order 3, 2, 4, 1.

62) **plea** — Rearrange letters 1, 3, 4, 5 in the order 3, 4, 1, 5.

63) **pier** — Rearrange letters 1, 4, 5, 6 in the order 6, 5, 4, 1.

64) **sale** — Rearrange letters 1, 2, 3, 6 in the order 6, 3, 1, 2.

65) **8** — 41 + 7 = 48, 48 = 8 × 6

66) **9** — 3 × 5 = 15, 15 = 24 – 9

67) **4** — 32 ÷ 4 = 8, 8 = 2 × 4

68) **6** — 13 + 11 – 6 = 18, 18 = 3 × 6

69) **10** — 9 × 5 + 5 = 50, 50 = 40 + 10

70) **5** — 24 ÷ 2 – 3 = 9, 9 = 4 + 5

71) **30** — 33 ÷ 3 × 2 = 22, 22 = 30 – 8

72) **23** — 7 × 4 ÷ 2 + 5 = 19, 19 = 23 – 4

73) **4** — 43 – 21 + 7 – 13 = 16, 16 = 4 × 4

74) **11** — 20 ÷ 5 × 7 ÷ 2 = 14, 14 = 25 – 11

Pages 79-84 — Assessment Test 4

1) **A** — In the poem it says there is a "tempest", which is another word for 'storm'.

2) **D** — In the poem it says that the sea king had a "wild and fitful life", which suggests that his life was full of adventure and had many ups and downs.

3) **B** — The sea king's "blood" suddenly stirs when he hears "the angry storm" outside.

4) **D** — In the poem it says that "they bore him from the couch of death / To his battle-ship to die".

5) **D** — In the poem it says that the sea king is wearing his "warrior robes", "sword" and "armour" when he dies, which suggests that he dresses as a soldier for his death.

6) **D** — In the poem it says that the sea king's pyre is "lit with many a mournful torch", which suggests that there are lots of people mourning him as he dies.

7) **B** — In this context, "spent" means 'used up', so the sea king is nearly at the end of his life.

8) **C** — This suggests that the sea king's hearing is being affected as he gets closer to death.

9) **B** — "splendour" is closest in meaning to 'magnificence'.

10) **C** — "wrathful" is closest in meaning to 'angry'.

11) **B** — 'Wang Zhenyi was an **influential** scholar'

12) **A** — 'scholar and **astronomer**'

13) **A** — 'women were **expected** to stay at home'

14) **B** — 'and **few** women received'

15) **D** — 'a formal **education**'

16) **C** — 'Zhenyi was **fortunate**'

17) **C** — 'born into an **affluent** family'

18) **A** — 'who **encouraged** her to study'

19) **B** — 'Her **chief** interests were Astronomy and Mathematics'

20) **D** — 'she was especially **fascinated** by eclipses'

21) **A** — 'to **simplify** difficult mathematical texts'

22) **C** — 'so that others could **understand** them more easily'

23) **A** — '**Besides** this'

24) **D** — 'she was a **talented** poet'

25) **above** — 'With its summit at 8,611 metres **above** sea level'

26) **exceeded** — 'its height **exceeded** only by Mount Everest'

Answers

27) **gigantic** — 'its freezing temperatures and **gigantic** size'

28) **dangerous** — 'one of the most **dangerous** mountains'

29) **failed** — 'the climbers who have **failed** to reach the summit'

30) **attempt** — 'Those brave enough to **attempt** the climb'

31) **lower** — 'the risk of snowstorms is **lower**'

32) **deadly** — 'the extreme cold can be **deadly**'

33) **harder** — 'as it is **harder** to breathe'

34) **challenge** — 'mountaineers take on the **challenge**'

35) **hectic** — 'peaceful' means 'calm', whereas 'hectic' means 'chaotic'.

36) **understate** — 'emphasise' means 'to stress', whereas 'understate' means 'to downplay'.

37) **elated** — 'miserable' means 'sad', whereas 'elated' means 'happy'.

38) **exhibit** — 'hide' means 'to cover up', whereas 'exhibit' means 'to show'.

39) **sceptical** — 'convinced' means 'sure', whereas 'sceptical' means 'unsure'.

40) **captivated** — 'distracted' means 'not paying attention to', whereas 'captivated' means 'paying full attention to'.

41) **disobey** — 'respect' means 'to follow a rule', whereas 'disobey' means 'to break a rule'.

42) **cease** — 'continue' means 'to carry on doing something', whereas 'cease' means 'to stop doing something'.

43) **bolster** — 'discourage' means 'to dishearten', whereas 'bolster' means 'to support'.

44) **gruelling** — 'effortless' means 'easy', whereas 'gruelling' means 'difficult'.

45) **clever ideas** — The hidden word is 'ride'.

46) **look indoors** — The hidden word is 'kind'.

47) **carriage arrived** — The hidden word is 'gear'.

48) **knee doing** — The hidden word is 'need'.

49) **until the** — The hidden word is 'tilt'.

50) **picnic eagerly** — The hidden word is 'nice'.

51) **35** — Multiply the outer numbers.

52) **13** — Find the mid-point between the two outer numbers by adding the outer numbers together and dividing the answer by 2.

53) **2** — Add the outer numbers together. Subtract 5.

54) **6** — Subtract the third number from the first number. Halve the answer.

55) **24** — Add the outer numbers together. Multiply by 3.

56) **m** — The new words are 'chop' and 'farm'.

57) **l** — The new words are 'fake' and 'pile'.

58) **d** — The new words are 'mist' and 'body'.

59) **u** — The new words are 'bond' and 'aunt'.

60) **i** — The new words are 'nose' and 'bait'.

61) **19** — The two previous numbers are added together to get the next number in the sequence, i.e. 2 + 5 = 7, 5 + 7 = 12 etc.

62) **16** — There are two sequences which alternate. In the first sequence, add 5 each time. In the second sequence, add 7 each time.

63) **48** — Multiply by ascending numbers: ×1, ×2, ×3, ×4.

64) **6** — There are two sequences which alternate. In the first sequence, divide by 2 each time. In the second sequence, multiply by 3 each time.

65) **16** — Subtract square numbers in descending order: -25, -16, -9, -4.

66) **sword wand** — They are the tools carried by each person.

67) **disgusting valued** — They are synonyms of 'vile' and 'prized'.

68) **see navigate** — They are what torches and compasses help someone to do.

69) **fluid gas** — They are the types of substances that water and air are.

70) **volume area** — They are the terms used to describe the total interior space of a cube and a square.

71) **peaceful poor** — They are antonyms of 'turbulent' and 'affluent'.

72) **4531** — T = 4, E = 5, A = 3, R = 1

73) **1325** — R = 1, A = 3, G = 2, E = 5

74) **GEAR** — G = 2, E = 5, A = 3, R = 1

Pages 85-90 — Assessment Test 5

1) **D** — The narrator says they "could feel the terrible weight of Da's sadness", which suggests that Da feels dejected.

2) **C** — The narrator is "amazed at Toaster's speed" and says that he worked with "mechanical precision".

3) **B** — There is no mention of how long the dust storm will last in the passage.

4) **A** — After the group continued working, it "wasn't too much later" when Da told them to stop.

5) **B** — In the passage it says that "Wild grit" was "stinging" their skin, so Ma's actions suggest that she wants to protect Hannah from being hurt.

6) **D** — The narrator says that "Only a tiny portion" of the corn will be harvested.

7) **A** — The narrator feels "the terrible weight of Da's sadness" that all of his hard work will be lost, which suggests that they feel sorry for him.

8) **D** — "exposed" is closest in meaning to 'bare'.

9) **C** — "vigour" is closest in meaning to 'energy'.

10) **B** — The phrase 'to be too generous in your estimation' means 'to overestimate something'. In the passage, Da expected there to be more time before the storm arrived.

11) **16** — Subtract the first number from the third number. Add 2.

12) **26** — Multiply the outer numbers. Subtract 2.

13) **42** — Multiply the outer numbers. Halve the answer.

14) **2** — Divide the third number by the first number. Halve the answer.

15) **10** — Add the outer numbers together. Divide by 4.

16) **29** — Find the mid-point between the two outer numbers.

17) **Sienna** — Sienna sees four sea creatures: a shark, an octopus, a stingray and a turtle.

18) **Wyatt** — Wyatt only has one activity planned: he is going to a party.

19) **bowed** — 'her head **bowed** against the fierce wind.'

20) **distance** — 'In the **distance**, the Ferris wheel towered'

21) **visitors** — 'all the **visitors** had gone home'

22) **forlorn** — 'the **forlorn** shrieks of gulls'

23) **against** — 'pounding of waves **against** the pier.'

24) **families** — 'all the happy **families**'

25) **building** — 'busily **building** sand castles

26) **winter** — 'for the **winter** at least'

27) **WOOD** — To get from the code to the word move the letters in the sequence +2, -2, +2, -2.

28) **KNOCK** — This is a mirror code, where each letter is an equal distance from the centre of the alphabet. P is 3 letters forward from the centre and K is 3 letters back; M is 1 letter back and N is 1 letter forward; L is 2 letters back and O is 2 letters forward; X is 11 letters forward and C is 11 letters back; P is 3 letters forward and K is 3 letters back.

29) **ATDCJ** — To get from the word to the code move the letters in the sequence -3, +2, -3, +2, -3.

30) **FMCPI** — To get from the word to the code move the letters in the sequence O, +1, +2, +3, +4.

31) **NIGHT** — This is a mirror code, where each letter is an equal distance from the centre of the alphabet. M is 1 letter back from the centre and N is 1 letter forward; R is 5 letters forward and I is 5 letters back; T is 7 letters forward and G is 7 letters back; S is 6 letters forward and H is 6 letters back; G is 7 letters back and T is 7 letters forward.

32) **RFFJZ** — To get from the word to the code move the letters in the sequence -1, -2, -3, -4, -5.

33) **IDEA** — To get from the code to the word move the letters in the sequence -1, -3, -5, -7.

34) **C** — 7 × 4 − 20 = 8, C = 8

35) **D** — 24 ÷ 3 × 2 = 16, D = 16

36) **C** — 8 × 4 ÷ 16 + 6 = 8, C = 8

37) **A** — 15 ÷ 3 + 8 − 10 = 3, A = 3

38) **fruit** — The words can be rearranged into the sentence 'My friend prefers apples to pears.'

39) **him** — The words can be rearranged into the sentence 'Their pet rabbit is called Flopsy.'

40) **most** — The words can be rearranged into the sentence 'The beach is my favourite place to visit.'

41) **cycled** — The words can be rearranged into the sentence 'We went for a bike ride last weekend.'

42) **danced** — The words can be rearranged into the sentence 'I wore my sequined dress to the party.'

43) **I** — The words can be rearranged into the sentence 'She asked me what my favourite colour was.'

44) **teach** — The words can be rearranged into the sentence 'It was warm and cosy in the classroom.'

45) **paws** — The words can be rearranged into the sentence 'The huge dog barked and wagged its tail.'

46) **we** — The words can be rearranged into the sentence 'I was asked to show the new girl around.'

47) **umbrella** — The words can be rearranged into the sentence 'We wanted to go outside but it was raining.'

48) **lid** — Take letter 4 from the first word, followed by letter 3 from the second word, then letter 1 from the first word.

49) **date** — Take letters 1 and 2 from the second word, followed by letter 3 from the first word, then letter 4 from the second word.

50) **set** — Take letters 1 and 3 from the second word, followed by letter 1 from the first word.

51) **task** — Take letters 4, 2 and 3 from the first word, followed by letter 4 from the second word.

52) **dies** — Take letter 4 from the second word, followed by letter 3 from the first word, then letters 2 and 5 from the second word.

53) **mark** — Take letters 1 and 2 from the first word, followed by letter 1 from the second word, then letter 3 from the first word.

54) **naps** — Take letters 4, 3 and 1 from the first word, followed by letter 5 from the second word.

55) **beat** — Take letters 1 and 2 from the second word, followed by letter 3 from the first word, then letter 4 from the second word.

56) **moderate drastic** — 'moderate' means 'average', whereas 'drastic' means 'extreme'.

57) **anchor uproot** — 'anchor' means 'to fix in place', whereas 'uproot' means 'to pull out of place'.

58) **passionate apathetic** — 'passionate' means 'with strong feeling', whereas 'apathetic' means 'lacking interest'.

59) **deplored exalted** — 'deplored' means 'disapproved of', whereas 'exalted' means 'praised'.

60) **recklessly gingerly** — 'recklessly' means 'without caution', whereas 'gingerly' means 'with great caution'.

61) **proficient incapable** — 'proficient' means 'able', whereas 'incapable' means 'unable'.

62) **appease provoke** — 'appease' means 'to subdue', whereas 'provoke' means 'to stir up'.

63) **19** — The number subtracted doubles each time: -1, -2, -4, -8, -16.

64) **14** — The numbers follow the sequence: +2, +1, O, -1, -2, -3.

65) **43** — Add prime numbers in ascending order: +2, +3, +5, +7, +11.

66) **3** — There are two sequences which alternate. In both sequences, the number halves each time.

67) **70** — Subtract square numbers in ascending order: -1, -4, -9, -16

68) **4** — Divide by ascending numbers: ÷1, ÷2, ÷3, ÷4.

69) **e** — The new words are 'flee', 'eel', 'pole' and 'elm'.

70) **n** — The new words are 'main', 'nine', 'tin' and 'nip'.

71) **l** — The new words are 'veil', 'look', 'meal' and 'last'.

72) **y** — The new words are 'jay', 'yet', 'icy' and 'yap'.

73) **m** — The new words are 'beam', 'mite', 'film' and 'mood'.

74) **r** — The new words are 'air', 'rap', 'ear' and 'ray'.

Pages 91-96 — Assessment Test 6

1) **D** — In the passage it says that the decision to build the Thames Barrier was taken following the "catastrophic flooding across the city" caused by the North Sea Flood.

2) **A** — The Queen opened the barrier a decade after engineers began work. Engineers began work on the barrier in 1974, so the Queen opened the barrier in 1984. The barrier took 8 years to build, so it was in use from 1982. This means the Queen opened the barrier two years after it was first in use.

3) **B** — The barrier has been closed about 200 times in the first 40 years since it was built. 200 divided by 40 is 5, so the average number of times it has been closed per year is 5.

4) **D** — The Environment Agency decide whether the barrier should close, which suggests that they operate it.

5) **C** — In the passage it says that the incident with the ship tested the "effectiveness of the barrier's design", which suggests it was built to be strong and resilient.

6) **B** — The barrier was built "upriver from central London" in order for it to be in a position to protect that part of the city from flooding.

7) **D** — In the passage it mentions "the largest of these gates", which suggests that some gates are bigger than others.

8) **C** — The barrier is opened again when the height of the river has reached an "equal level" on either side of the gates.

9) **D** — The barrier was built to be closed during bad weather when there is a risk of flooding. The barrier closed 50 times in 2013-14, which suggests that the weather was particularly stormy during that time.

10) **C** — The barrier was intended to last from 1982, when construction finished, to 2030. This is a period of 48 years, so it was built to last less than 50 years.

11) **3564** — S = 3, E = 5, A = 6, T = 4

12) **2615** — R = 2, A = 6, C = 1, E = 5

13) **STAR** — S = 3, T = 4, A = 6, R = 2

14) **KR** — The first letter in the pair moves back 4 letters, the second letter moves back 2 letters.

15) **LT** — The first letter in the pair moves back 4 letters, the second letter moves forward 2 letters.

16) **ZC** — The first letter in the pair moves back 5 letters, the second letter moves forward 7 letters.

17) **LW** — The first letter in the pair moves back 2 letters, the second letter moves forward 5 letters.

18) **LO** — AZ, FU and GT are mirror pairs, where the two letters are an equal distance from the centre of the alphabet. F is 5 letters forward from A, so the missing mirror pair is LO, because L is 5 letters forward from G, and O is its mirror pair.

19) **TF** — The first letter in the pair moves back 9 letters, the second letter moves forward 13 letters.

20) **astute** — Both words mean 'quick-witted'.

21) **devilment** — Both words mean 'playful bad behaviour'.

22) **conscientious** — Both words mean 'very careful'.

23) **compelled** — Both words mean 'obliged'.

24) **scrutinise** — Both words mean 'to analyse'.

25) **strenuous** — Both words mean 'requiring lots of effort'.

26) **inherent** — Both words mean 'already existing'.

27) **accomplished** — Both words mean 'expert'.

28) **C** — 16 − 12 + 4 = 8, C = 8

29) **E** — 3 × 9 + 6 − 11 = 22, E = 22

30) **B** — 5 × 6 ÷ 2 − 10 = 5, B = 5

31) **C** — 18 ÷ 2 × 4 ÷ 6 = 6, C = 6

32) **A** — 16 ÷ 8 × 12 + 2 − 24 = 2, A = 2

33) **frivolous** — 'serious' means 'important', whereas 'frivolous' means 'trivial'.

34) **indefinite** — 'limited' means 'restricted in number', whereas 'indefinite' means 'endless'.

35) **thoughtless** — 'reasoned' means 'based on logic', whereas 'thoughtless' means 'not based on anything'.

36) **distressing** — 'reassuring' means 'comforting', whereas 'distressing' means 'upsetting'.

37) **unintentional** — 'premeditated' means 'planned', whereas 'unintentional' means 'unplanned'.

38) **convoluted** — 'uncomplicated' means 'simple', whereas 'convoluted' means 'difficult to understand'.

39) **acknowledge** — 'disregard' means 'ignore', whereas 'acknowledge' means 'recognise'.

40) **irresolute** — 'stubborn' means 'not easily influenced', whereas 'irresolute' means 'uncertain'.

41) **A** — 'I **stepped** onto the platform'

42) **B** — '**and** surveyed'

43) **B** — 'surveyed the **view**.'

44) **D** — '**fuelled** by a fear of the unknown.'

45) **C** — 'Before **leaping** off the edge'

46) **B** — 'I felt **immense** excitement'

47) **C** — 'excitement **mingled** with anticipation'

48) **A** — '**for** what I was about to do.'

49) **D** — 'with the **intention** of'

50) **C** — '**conquer** my fear of heights.'

51) **B** — 'Before I **knew** it'

52) **D** — 'I was **soaring** rapidly'

53) **A** — 'It was **undoubtedly** the most exhilarating thing'

54) **C** — 'I'd ever **experienced**.'

55) **feast arrived** — The hidden word is 'star'.

56) **cover your** — The hidden word is 'very'.

57) **puffin chick** — The hidden word is 'inch'.

58) **The apples** — The hidden word is 'heap'.

59) **am eating** — The hidden word is 'meat'.

60) **chilli on** — The hidden word is 'lion'.

61) **do great** — The hidden word is 'ogre'.

62) **We are** — The hidden word is 'wear'.

63) **ASH** — The complete word is SMASHED.

64) **ARC** — The complete word is PARCELS.

65) **LOW** — The complete word is FOLLOWED.

66) **INK** — The complete word is TWINKLE.

67) **ROB** — The complete word is PROBLEM.

68) **ANT** — The complete word is QUANTITY.

69) **RUG** — The complete word is STRUGGLE.

70) **RUN** — The complete word is GRUNTED.

71) **OAT** — The complete word is GLOATING.

72) **HER** — The complete word is CHERISH.

73) **D** — Baljit came first, then Omar finished second ahead of Georgina who was faster than Fiona. Fiona was faster than Davina, so Davina must have finished last.

74) **C** — If Patrick bought the same amount of presents as Hetty and Jamal together, then Patrick must have bought at least 3 presents. Aurianne bought one more present than Patrick, so she must have bought more than 3 presents.

Pages 97-102 — Assessment Test 7

1) **C** — The narrator says they "love the hour before takeoff". This suggests that they have previous experience of air travel, as they know what it is like.

2) **B** — The narrator says that while waiting to go to their gate, they spend their time looking at the "families" around them, as well as other people like the "bachelorette" and the "athlete".

3) **D** — The narrator describes going up to the gate as a "clumsy procedure", which suggests that they think it's an awkward process.

4) **B** — The mother is "waiting to be called up early", which suggests that she will be allowed to board the plane first.

5) **B** — In the poem it says that the executive has "worked for the pleasure" of going on the plane, which suggests that he is going on holiday rather than on a business trip.

6) **C** — The narrator does not mention their destination.

7) **A** — "ragtag" means 'untidy and disordered'.

8) **B** — In the poem, the athlete is "perched" on the edge of his seat ready to react to the signal to board, just like a seal is "trained" to "plunge" into the water when commanded to.

9) **B** — "summoned" is closest in meaning to 'called'.

10) **D** — "monstrous" is closest in meaning to 'colossal'.

11) **sole**mn — 'jolly' means 'cheerful', whereas 'solemn' means 'serious'.

12) **tragic** — 'uplifting' means 'very happy', whereas 'tragic' means 'very sad'.

13) **drench**ed — 'parched' means 'dry', whereas 'drenched' means 'wet'.

14) **preci**ous — 'worthless' means 'lacking value', whereas 'precious' means 'having value'.

15) **discreet** — 'tactless' means 'careless', whereas 'discreet' means 'careful'.

16) **radiant** — 'dim' means 'lacking light', whereas 'radiant' means 'bright'.

17) **forthright** — 'secretive' means 'reserved', whereas 'forthright' means 'open'.

18) **sensitive** — 'numb' means 'lacking feeling', whereas 'sensitive' means 'feeling easily'.

19) **vigilant** — 'inattentive' means 'oblivious', whereas 'vigilant' means 'watchful'.

20) **ambitious** — 'idle' means 'lazy', whereas 'ambitious' means 'determined'.

21) **riveting** — 'boring' means 'uninteresting', whereas 'riveting' means 'interesting'.

22) **fleeting** — 'lasting' means 'unending', whereas 'fleeting' means 'momentary'.

23) **dogged   tenacious** — Both words mean 'resolute'.

24) **combine   unite** — Both words mean 'to put together'.

25) **mock   deride** — Both words mean 'to make fun of'.

26) **crowded   jammed** — Both words mean 'packed'.

27) **voyage   expedition** — Both words mean 'a journey'.

28) **45** — The number added increases by 2 each time: +2, +4, +6, +8, +10.

29) **10** — The two previous numbers are subtracted from each other to get the next number, i.e. 50 – 30 = 20.

30) **9** — These are square numbers in descending order, i.e. 7 × 7 = 49, 6 × 6 = 36 etc.

31) **44** — The number added triples each time: +1, +3, +9, +27.

32) **8** — There are two sequences which alternate. In the first you divide by 2 each time, and in the second you multiply by 3 each time.

33) **6** — There are two sequences which alternate. In the first you subtract 15 each time, and in the second you divide by 2 each time.

34) **intend** — 'intend' is the only correctly spelled word that can be made.

35) **beside** — 'beside' is the only correctly spelled word that can be made.

36) **factor** — 'factor' is the only correctly spelled word that can be made.

37) **lipstick** — 'lipstick' is the only correctly spelled word that can be made.

38) **thinking** — 'thinking' is the only correctly spelled word that can be made.

39) **rampage** — 'rampage' is the only correctly spelled word that can be made.

40) **format** — 'format' is the only correctly spelled word that can be made.

41) **covered** — 'covered' is the only correctly spelled word that can be made.

42) **4156** — D = 4, A = 1, L = 5, E = 6

43) **5124** — L = 5, A = 1, N = 2, D = 4

44) **NAME** — N = 2, A = 1, M = 3, E = 6

45) **3642** — S = 3, O = 6, A = 4, P = 2

46) **2615** — P = 2, O = 6, U = 1, T = 5

47) **SOUP** — S = 3, O = 6, U = 1, P = 2

48) **PATS** — P = 2, A = 4, T = 5, S = 3

49) **trotter** — The other three are all body parts of birds.

50) **illustration** — The other three are written features of books.

51) **puddle** — The other three are all frozen forms of water.

52) **core** — The other three are words for the outer layer of fruit.

53) **swing** — The other three mean 'to rotate'.

54) **indigo** — The other three are all shades of red.

55) **shoreline** — The other three are places where boats are moored.

56) **tractor** — The other three are vehicles that are pulled.

57) **pamphlet** — The other three all mean 'a piece of paper'.

58) **output** — The other three are types of processes.

59) **bank** — 'bank' can mean 'a place that stores and lends money' or 'a tall mound'.

60) **succeed** — 'succeed' can mean 'to take the place of' or 'to do well'.

61) **contract** — 'contract' can mean 'an arrangement' or 'to come down with an illness'.

62) **console** — 'console' can mean 'a piece of electronic equipment' or 'to comfort'.

63) **deliberate** — 'deliberate' can mean 'intentional' or 'to think'.

64) **inclined** — 'inclined' can mean 'likely to choose' or 'sloped'.

65) **refuse** — 'refuse' can mean 'to turn down' or 'garbage'.

66) **offence** — 'offence' can mean 'bad feelings' or 'a wrongdoing'.

67) **KF** — The first letter in the pair moves forward 7 letters, the second letter moves back 2 letters.

68) **OU** — VE and WD are mirror pairs, where the two letters are an equal distance from the centre of the alphabet. O is the mirror of L and U is the mirror of F.

69) **AT** — The first letter in the pair moves back 6 letters, the second letter moves forward 5 letters.

70) **EF** — The first letter in the pair moves forward 4 letters, the second letter moves back 3 letters.

71) **IK** — CX and UF are mirror pairs, where the two letters are an equal distance from the centre of the alphabet. I is the mirror of R and K is the mirror of P.

72) **NI** — The first letter in the pair moves forward 10 letters, the second letter moves back 7 letters.

73) **VE** — QJ, TG and SH are mirror pairs, where the two letters are an equal distance from the centre of the alphabet. T is 3 letters forward from Q, so the missing mirror pair is VE because V is 3 letters forward from S, and E is its mirror pair.

74) **MC** — OL and RI are mirror pairs, where the two letters are an equal distance from the centre of the alphabet. M is the mirror of N and C is the mirror of X.

Pages 103-108 — Assessment Test 8

1) **A** — The unanswered questions at the start of the text engage the reader's interest in the topic.

2) **D** — In the passage it says that the Ice Palace is "the cave's crowning glory".

3) **C** — In the passage it says that ice caves are "scattered across the globe", which means they are found around the world.

4) **C** — In the passage it says that tourists can reach the ice cave "in an array of ways".

5) **B** — In the passage it says that the climb to the cave's entrance is "arduous" and is only tackled by "more intrepid tourists".

6) **B** — In the passage it says the ice sheets look "like sapphires and diamonds", but there are no actual gemstones in the cave.

7) **D** — In the passage it says that the cave in the Mer de Glace glacier in France is "man-made", so this means it wasn't formed naturally.

8) **A** — In the passage it says that the Eisriesenwelt cave is "Unrivalled in its proportions", which means it is the largest ice cave in the world.

9) **A** — "phenomenon" is closest in meaning to 'occurrence'.

10) **B** — "predominantly" is closest in meaning to 'principally'.

11) **Harvey** — Harvey went on five rides: the roller coaster, the log flume, the pirate ship, the dodgems and the waltzer.

12) **Eli** — Eli saw two birds: a robin and a wren.

13) **pleasantly   obnoxiously** — 'pleasantly' means 'in a friendly way', whereas 'obnoxiously' means 'in a rude way'.

14) **confident   apprehensive** — 'confident' means 'certain', whereas 'apprehensive' means 'unsure'.

15) **acquire   surrender** — 'acquire' means 'to get something', whereas 'surrender' means 'to give something up'.

16) **unfathomable   intelligible** — 'unfathomable' means 'not understandable', whereas 'intelligible' means 'understandable'.

17) **companionship   solitude** — 'companionship' means 'the feeling of being with others', whereas 'solitude' means 'the state of being alone'.

18) **C** — 'Cannons boomed **ferociously**'

19) **A** — 'the ship **pitched** forward'

20) **B** — 'and seconds **later**'

21) **A** — 'the pirates were **on** board'

22) **D** — '**quivering** with fear'

23) **C** — 'rolled **behind** some barrels'

24) **A** — 'to **conceal** herself'

25) **D** — 'She **could** see a man'

26) **B** — 'looming **ominously** over her shipmates'

27) **C** — 'his sword **glinting** menacingly'

28) **C** — 'She felt **helpless**'

29) **B** — 'she heard him **barking** orders'

30) **D** — 'at his **petrified** prisoners'

31) **B** — 'The situation was **perilous**'

32) **monument** — 'a type of Stone Age **monument**'

33) **throughout** — 'are found **throughout** the British Isles'

34) **particularly** — '**particularly** common in hilly areas'

35) **construction** — 'The reasons for their **construction** are still unknown'

36) **religious** — 'they were used for **religious** rituals'

37) **remarkable** — 'a **remarkable** stone circle'

38) **overlooking** — 'a huge stone **overlooking** the circle'

39) **prehistoric** — 'which has **prehistoric** carvings on it'

40) **numerous** — 'There are **numerous** local legends'

41) **puzzling** — 'linked to its **puzzling** presence'

42) **u** — The new words are 'prod' and 'four'.

43) **s** — The new words are 'tuck' and 'self'.

44) **o** — The new words are 'shut' and 'logo'.

45) **p** — The new words are 'lain' and 'spun'.

46) **i** — The new words are 'fled' and 'claim'.

47) **r** — The new words are 'chat' and 'front'.

48) **optimistic   dismal** — They are synonyms of 'hopeful' and 'gloomy'.

49) **guidance   caution** — They are synonyms of 'advice' and 'warning'.

50) **deny   contradict** — They are antonyms of 'confirm' and 'agree'.

51) **academy   army** — They are what a class and a regiment are part of.

52) **chaos   structure** — They are synonyms of 'disorder' and 'organisation'.

53) **5624** — R = 5, U = 6, S = 2, T = 4

54) **1364** — B = 1, O = 3, U = 6, T = 4

55) **OUST** — O = 3, U = 6, S = 2, T = 4

56) **one** — Remove letters 2, 3 and 4, leaving the remaining letters in the order 1, 5, 6.

57) **nit** — Rearrange letters 3, 5, 6 in the order 3, 6, 5.

58) **fees** — Rearrange letters 2, 4, 5, 7 in the order 7, 5, 2, 4.

59) **net** — Rearrange letters 3, 4, 5 in the order 5, 4, 3.

60) **rate** — Rearrange letters 3, 5, 6, 7 in the order 7, 3, 5, 6.

61) **k** — The new words are 'beak', 'kick', 'spark' and 'kit'.

62) **f** — The new words are 'surf', 'frown', 'calf' and 'fund'.

63) **t** — The new words are 'fist', 'tow', 'but' and 'tire'.

64) **a** — The new words are 'media', 'aloud', 'pasta' and 'alone'.

65) **t** — The new words are 'fort', 'task', 'glut' and 'trip'.

66) **y** — The new words are 'deny', 'yet', 'defy', 'year'.

67) **status** — Both words mean 'reputation'.

68) **curb** — Both words mean 'to limit'.

69) **craven** — Both words mean 'timid'.

70) **forcibly** — Both words mean 'forcefully'.

71) **amplify** — Both words mean 'magnify'.

72) **morose** — Both words mean 'mournful'.

73) **lamentable** — Both words mean 'unfortunate'.

74) **fabrication** — Both words mean 'a lie'.

Progress Chart

Use this chart to keep track of your scores for the <u>Assessment Tests</u>.

You can do each test more than once — download extra answer sheets from cgpbooks.co.uk/11plus/answer-sheets or scan the QR code on the right.

Answer Sheets

	First Go	**Second Go**	**Third Go**
Test 1	Date: Score:	Date: Score:	Date: Score:
Test 2	Date: Score:	Date: Score:	Date: Score:
Test 3	Date: Score:	Date: Score:	Date: Score:
Test 4	Date: Score:	Date: Score:	Date: Score:
Test 5	Date: Score:	Date: Score:	Date: Score:
Test 6	Date: Score:	Date: Score:	Date: Score:
Test 7	Date: Score:	Date: Score:	Date: Score:
Test 8	Date: Score:	Date: Score:	Date: Score:

Look back at your scores once you've done all the <u>Assessment Tests</u>.
Each test is out of <u>74 marks</u>.

Work out which kind of mark you scored most often:

0-43 marks — Go back to <u>basics</u> and work on your <u>question technique</u>.

44-62 marks — You're nearly there — go back over the questions you found <u>tricky</u>.

63-74 marks — You're a <u>Verbal Reasoning star</u>.